This is brilliant!

C000257085

OTHER TITLES IN THE *MASKS* SERIES

IS BEAUTY GOOD

IS BEAUTY GOOD

Rosalind Belben

SERPENT'S
TAIL

The publishers thank Kathy Acker, Mark Ainley, Martin Chalmers, John Kraniauskas, Bob Lumley, Enrico Palandri, Kate Pullinger, Antonio Sanchez for their advice and assistance.

British Library Cataloguing in Publication Data
Belben, Rosalind.
　　Is beauty good.
　　I. Title.
　　823'.914　[F]

ISBN 1-85242-153-3

First published 1989 by
Serpent's Tail, Unit 4, Blackstock Mews, London N4

Typeset in 10/12 pt Medieval Roman by
AKM Associates (UK) Ltd, Southall, London

Printed in Great Britain by
WBC Print (Bristol) Ltd.

Contents

Das Berliner Künstlerprogramm des DAAD, The Royal Literary Fund, Literarisches Colloquium Berlin and particular friends and relations of mine are thanked, very much.

R.B.

THE INSATIABLE WHEEL

The Nightmare

And so, as Fritz is going home in one of those elderly Berlin trams they keep in the east, he stares from the window and is suddenly hit, he thinks, by paradox: if what is ugly didn't strike me as ugly, he thinks, I shouldn't mind staring at it, I shouldn't feel pained by my journey home; if I were indifferent, if each building, old and new, struck me indifferently, my journey home would be not a matter of seeing but of being jolted and dreaming of coffee and biscuits and sometimes cake; and my journey would be soothing; and my journey would be a rest, since I must be weary. If we are so susceptible to what we perceive as beautiful, and to what we perceive as offending that sense, is beauty good? Fritz asks himself.

And, sitting, or standing, with binoculars, in his uniform, at an angular window in a tower above a dirty white wall, he says to his friend, that woman, there, who has come by train through fields full of mist and fog and dim sunlight, full of the early morning, when shapes of horses loom out of the passing countryside and retreat, that woman has thought in the train about horses; and how horses will stare into the distance and make contented noises with their nostrils, seem to like a view, a fine day, a landscape of quietly-moving things, seem to like sun, sun cool enough to warm and yet bring no flies; seem to have, don't you reckon, a kind of aesthetic appreciation of what's around them; to have an idea of beauty. That woman there? his friend says. Certainly, says Fritz.

He says to his friend, what use is a sense of beauty, if it brings also a sense of ugliness and repulsion and distress when we're faced with things which offend it? And why do we wrinkle our metaphorical noses at meat that's creeping with blow-fly maggots, whereas it is actually beautiful to see how rotten meat is cleaned up and eaten down.

What do horses dream of, I wonder, he says; of fine views? and clean crisp air? and sun on their backs, a frosty morning ablaze with scent? We look at dogs as they dream and watch their legs working and hear their yapping, or the grunting echo of a whoof from a big dog, and their skin twitches, they pant, and we know they are running after a rabbit or rushing round gorse bushes peering in, braving the prickles; but what do horses dream of?

We feel pain, says Fritz, because we need to feel pain, it saves us from being burnt, or hurt, or from walking blindly into danger, breaking a bone; but what does a sense of beauty save us from; what purpose is there in our being coruscated by passing uglinesses; there is little that is moral about beauty; or does it reinforce somehow our notion of moral good: is beauty good?

Why must we describe to ourselves continually what we see? Buildings and people and vegetables and clothing, a dusty wind blowing in the streets, why do we have to remark on it at all, poverty and misery and greed and unkindness, illness and depression. Why do we bother? Why do we bother even to be tired, and lonely. And if we are so hideous to them, why do they come to gawp at us?

I go home, Fritz says, having looked through binoculars at ugly people all day, seeing all the ugly people, all the ugly buildings, all the ugliness, and some better things, pretty people, handsome buildings, sights agreeable to my eye, home to my mother, who is plain but loved and familiar, to my supper which is the same, to my bed which is comfortable, holds me in its arms, to dream.

I swallow a gold crown eating supper, so in the morning have to take my shit apart, and the next morning too, and that my sister finds quite nauseatingly ugly, though she doesn't have to see it, and which I, interested only in the beauty of finding it, my crown, don't find at all appalling.

Where would we be if we didn't shit, I say to my sister, it's a harmless method of disposal. Harmless, she says, carrying all those diseases? Worse, far worse, I tell her, if the diseases had to come out through our mouths.

If there is a purpose in a thing, I think, does that render it beautiful, the scavenging animals, the blow-flies, the worms and the maggots?

We have mechanisms for neutralising, Fritz says to his friend. I wonder if we don't have too strong a mechanism for neutralising in our minds the ugly or the sordid, the brutal and the cruel, we come to terms with it too easily, and it's a mistake.

We have minds which swallow and digest and re-gurgitate the unwholesome as wholesomeness.

I don't suppose horses do that.

I dream of diving into a black pool, in which, very far down, is a ruin of girders, a trap, holding some treasure or secret I want, without a thought, to get; but with my second dive I am suddenly afraid, imagining how it would be if I entered the tangle, the box-like structure of girders, and wanted to breathe, to rise to the surface, and was trapped, by girders, by my panic, having to clamber, and the murkiness of the water was most unattractive. I couldn't see why I had to dive in and enter the tangle and retrieve the secret or the treasure of it, the beauty within, so I refused to dive, I shirked it.

I wonder if horses dream like that? he says. I don't suppose so.

If horses? or that woman?, she's still there, says his friend.

Air Ride

It isn't the messenger that has to walk, but the message, says Sepp. I understand, clasping his brass one, because I play an instrument, sitting in a gondola swinging high over the rising, falling mountain, I understand a little music, I know then, I know, he says making the gondola swim in the air, why else do we meet once a year on the mountain, whom do you imagine we play to, the faithful, the crowd, we play to the things that hear, things in the mountains, there are things in the mountains that hear, we used to trudge up, three and three quarter hours with a tuba, but we have legs for tuba and cornet alike, we don't leap with a tuba, when we arrive the instrument, that leaps, and all around there are ears.

And suppose those ears do prefer Bach. Well, they listen quite politely to Johann Strauß, they are grateful for anything, those ears are, with cow-bells and the breeze and the howling wind for company, and any music sounds strange and beautiful that high, in such a remote place, as rare as the air is, move a space away, out of sight, and the music arrives in a thin stream, a watery noise, isolated, as if borne on a single corridor of the air, a ribbon of music, not Bach, a tiny, dear little stream, and the gondola swings at his pun, most mysterious.

That's the trouble the world over, he says. Nobody listens. Nature listens, but nature is helpless to act, nature is at the mercy. Isn't she! I think, so long as someone bothers to take a tuba to the top of the mountain, so long as, oh! there's my wife, she has to walk, she's frightened of gondola travel, nothing would possess her to ride so easily down. Imagine, she never sees what the tuba sees, sitting in the last of the sun, what an instrument, above the tops of the trees, not every tuba is enabled, to shine in the sun, a wonderful shining that darts off across the mountain-flank.

I'm pretty plump, the tuba and I, we're both plump, and there is more of us to reflect the sun. I'm sure the sun likes us, even if fat is unfashionable, fashions do reach us in the mountains, the same as sun, the sun is stronger and the fashions are weaker, we keep tradition, we've settled for tradition, and fashion sways us little. Sepp clasps his tuba more firmly around the waist. His wife is a speck among other gondola-fearing specks, in bright cotton frocks among the trees, and then hidden from view. That speck is my wife, he says, waving at it. All the specks turn their faces up as the gondola glides over their heads, they look like so many flowers, he says.

You may listen, because you are stuck in a gondola with my tuba and me. But I tell you. Tubas have a satisfying life, being hugged, shining, making sunlight dart. I tell you, whatever it is that the bearer with your password has, it is getting terribly hindered by all these folk with their longing to talk, to chatter, to rabbit on about this and that, whether beauty is good, until the message itself is crying out in a little babyish voice, let me on my journey, let me be transferred to yet another hand, let me smother all the chatterboxes in the world, so I may at last arrive, since that is what I am for, to arrive, to be understood, not held in a clammy hand, but understood, my import fulfilled.

I don't fool myself, he says, squirming to make the tuba comfortable. I adore playing, yet I am not important, we should be listening to our instruments and not to ourselves. Hasn't it always been so? Innumerable messages, throughout history, that never quite arrive. In the mountains we can hear one another, and what do we do? We call back, we are drunk on the sound of our own voices, how they carry, and for practical purposes the carrying is of use. If we speak only of goats, if we pass the time of day, that's fine. In the world, in history, there are bigger messages, and our failing to listen, to understand, makes great nanny-goats of all of us. The dear Lord has enough trouble with his. Passwords are a mistake, they take on an aura and the message whose path they are there to smooth is smothered. These mountains have seen a lot of fighting, undeciphered things pass to and fro.

And tucked beneath the steep drop, my summer hut nestles in the trapped sun, the waterfall is busy, and the breeze tinkling. High above us the lake sits, balanced, precarious, and with the slightest push, it seems, a falling rock, could tip out and run all down the valley, the many valleys, to the plains. That was where the forked stick started, by a hidden lake, a fragile, dark blue water, from there a password is needed, where peace is, farther is not peace, is strife, muddle, and bitterness, and aggrieved parties, hardly a whisper breaks its stillness, the green of the turf, and the blue, the freshness nourishes the heart, I fear there is a thing about a tuba, it makes one lyrical, one sees snow on the peaks, a mountain with a glacier, white snow, blue sky, no clashes, no jealousy, no trampling, no world, not a shred of ugliness, cows and goats, that's all, and one wonders! In winter it is even more beautiful. The first stretch is the wildest. I and my wife and the tuba, we dwell there in the summer, we are being thrust from our home by the conflict. The unfortunate message, how it cries, and weeps, and tears its hair; and no one listens; there are ears in the mountains but they can't reply. The tuba rolls as the gondola bumps home itself. At least we, we at least, have arrived. He says, I don't understand, I don't understand conflict, or life, or my wife, only mountains, music, messages. And we are bound to think that's sad. It's bed-time, he says to his instrument. Good night to you!

Good night! I love her, she likes frocks, what is a frock, a piece of bunting, how can a frock speak, she says frocks do a lot of talking, frocks are chatterers, frippery chatterers, and she has no end of time for frocks, the more highly-coloured the better.

I am far from home, thinks Kai, so far from the home I expected to stay close to. And whoever would have believed it, a fairy tale, we are shoulder to shoulder with troops from other unlikely countries, fighting like babies in the mountains, to liberate the people, whoever would have dreamt that.

They say to him, come, friend, dream up a watchword, a password, our messenger must be on his way and we need a watchword. Shall we call out, a cock and bull story, or the sky is blue tomorrow, or balls bounce high, or, simply, myrtle? Kai is perplexed. He remembers his companion of a long time ago, that companion who was always speaking of beauty, is beauty good, and so forth. Kai says, why not? Is beauty good. They laugh. Friend, they say, it will do very well.

He was a splendid fellow, a contented, serene man, who busied himself with whimsical questions. And not so whimsical. How the world would be, perhaps better off, without aesthetic sensibilities.

And why one person's taste is sound, and another's false; and how a third person can see that, and a fourth not. Integrity!

His mother, whom I met often, had a disturbing twitch, a tic, and no one understood its source, for she wasn't bothered unduly by life, or nervous.

Her poor face went into a contortion, one had to look aside for several minutes.

I can imagine, says Kai, the poor earth might feel a similar tic, don't you think earth tremors might be the poor little earth's tic, though it's hard to see why she should feel so put upon, and maligned. Is this how she responds to our tillage and ministrations and our appreciation of her milk and honey, her oil and minerals, her harvest, her capabilities?

I was acquainted with a woman once, Kai says, and no matter how often one stroked her, and wolfed down her delicious cooking, and admired her pretty face, and her neck, and her feet, her legs, she would quiver with resentment, it's possible the poor dear earth does that too. They laugh.

Look around you, he says, what are these mountains for, what are breasts for, unless to make us mourn them and feel miserable on the plains. If one is a soldier, why does one have to speak of breasts, why do soldiers interminably dwell on breasts. It's an archetypal pre-occupation. It all stems from infantry training, being taught to make the best use of cover, whatever cover nature vouchsafes, crouching behind humps, the least rise in the terrain, and having the confidence to assume the rise gives one shelter, whereas one is vulnerable indeed. An absurdity.

And fox-holes. What do they remind you of? A whole battle can be organised over a woman's body. Woods and forests, hills and crannies, tears for streams, and drenching rain, sniper fire, one can cook up a fine sortie on a woman. In the ravine between her upper lip and lower, where lipstick streaks the rock, like iron ore and copper and rust, and moss clings to her cheeks, in the ravine one must lie, without coughing, without stirring, without water or food, rifle cocked on the corner, on one's belly.

And bayonets. Aren't we instructed to thrust them, with a blood-curdling yell, still, what antiquated actions, into a straw stomach. And if we're lucky, yells the counterpart also. Are we not instructed to that yell? And be disappointed if it doesn't come?

Fritz, my old companion, was a dreamer. He was always

dreaming, and telling me his dreams. Yet I dream. I dreamt I was a rabbit and my burrow fell in on me, I was suffocating and still I thought, I am a rabbit, now why should being a rabbit be more important a feature than suffocating. Shall I be thinking, I am a rabbit, when I snuff it? I hope not. They laugh. It can't be so wonderful to be a rabbit. And with my rabbit's eyes I could see gypsies, making tin pots, in the field, and water flew down the stream. Water is so calming. I like to see water as some like to see flowers.

And now we have to make a pincer movement, a manoeuvre which is beautiful, and we shall feel happy, if it comes off, as my companion's mother said she felt after her face had contorted, it re-defined her thoughts, her world, her circumstances, imagine having a disorder, a facial cataclysm, which is profoundly satisfying. But one had to look away while it was happening.

Human beings are so full of longings. I myself would rather be without longings than without beauty. I am far from home, and, for myself, I could do without longing. You laugh, because you all are. Aren't we all, always, even on our own doorstep. For myself, I could do without longing. If I may speak for myself, it is only, I think, please don't laugh, after one has grown out of all such nonsense that one can settle to the business in hand.

Swansong, Beetroot Song

And it all comes back to grate at one, I don't know, am I the cheese, the fingers, the grater, all are gnawed at. I sit up to my neck in yellow mud, or I plunge my arms in and out of ice-cold water, I'm lying half the day in hay baths, and letting the herbs do something to me, and what? what do they do? for how long? what for?

It's such a sad search, you never find it, if it doesn't accompany you, or only for a brief while.

I drank carrot juice, beetroot juice. Disgusting. It seemed undignified, to be so desperate as to drink beetroot juice. Yet people do it without a second thought. They say if you want to get well you have to have no hoity-toity notions.

I've always had hoity-toity notions, or what are viewed as being so, it's in my character. Then my mother-in-law said, you would rather succumb, entirely, she talks in euphemisms, than drink beetroot juice. It may be. I'd be distressed to imagine I had to swallow a lot of beetroot juice. I've never been fond of beetroots. It's fine if you're fond of beetroots. The trivial.

I hear the hostilities, as my mother-in-law would call it, started over a ceiling? A modest ceiling!

I can cope with hay baths, and freezing water, there is grandeur in hay, in water, in grasses. Beetroot are vulgar. And everyone becomes bored, health and the lack of it is terribly boring, vitality is what, she says, and stops.

I was fond of a swan. I used to visit the swan I was fond of in the stream. It was a quite wild swan, a he-swan, not tame but unafraid, as swans are, living alone. He would sit, swim, float, difficult to describe what a large swan does in shallow water, and sleep with his head tucked over his back, the beak resting in the pinion feathers, he would turn his eye towards me, listening, and one's heart goes out to a swan alone, without a mate, I often went to talk to him, in the little stream, and he paddled, snatching at the watery grass, less, and slept with his head on his wing, more, and his neck grew weaker, could hardly hold his head up, and I thought only of my friendship, my kinship, with a swan, but his friendliness was his sickness, he was mortally ill, and all I dreamt of was myself, I perceived nothing, even if there was nothing I could have done, these swans swallow the fishermen's lead and are poisoned.

I can't bear it, how one imagines one knows everything! And how creatures still have to give, go on giving, when they're mortally ill. I'd like that kind of dignity. Yet they accuse my unconscious, they accuse it of death wishes and of having little will. I have will. I'd like to be free to exercise it. For one is never free, if a human being, one is always accused, fingers point from all the corners, and the grating continues. If we were without cheese-graters we'd be lost in the kitchen. It's tedious, never to be well, and to be seriously unwell is even more tedious. I'm a human being, so instead of sitting, or swimming, or lying on my breast in a stream, I make journeys, to mud baths, sulphur spas, to the mountains, seeking cures and healings, or a little, little, dear little respite.

I remember my swan. To have one friend whose beak didn't open to speak of beetroot juice!

Beetroot juice is what comes out of people's minds and mouths when they're embarrassed. It spews out. A swan feels no embarrassment, not for being alone, not for his silence, not for being unable to hold his head up. But swans have been known, if with a mate, to hold the dying mate's head up out of the water, so it dies and doesn't drown. Human beings force one to question one's unconscious, at the very moment one would prefer to hold it silently in one's own beak.

If there is a healing, it is in the water which springs out of the rocks, full of minerals, so strong it can burn on one's cheeks. You have only to wet your face with it to feel the burning of it onto the cheeks.

The swan, does he have hope, do swans live in terms of hope, and search, and desperation, perhaps they do. I travel, with neither hope nor despair, to the mountains, I have a desire to sit or swim in the stream, and be misunderstood. I want to be utterly misunderstood, like my swan, it is a grace, to be ignored in one's distress, not to have beetroot juice thrust down one's throat or to be...but I believe they don't attempt to extract the lead, it is by then too late, the poisoning is slow, like the painful search for one's health, what they do is to take X-rays and look at the lead, sitting wherever it sits, in the gizzard, in the crop, they look at it and they shake their heads and they will have cared, for the swan, for swans, they do care, they persuade the fishermen not to use lead, people with beetroot juice and the naughty unconscious on the brain, they care, they all care, we buy care, I should have cared for my swan, by not caring I let my swan give me a feeling of companionship, and that sense of a wild creature's being, life. It is all nonsensical, it is one's own poor little head which constructs all these things.

And we travel to the mountains, she repeats, from the four corners of the earth, hoping more and more urgently for what the mountains possess to be given to us, it is not of course. The flowers of the alm are trampled, people are shot, without the chance to sit in a stream, or swim, we human beings aren't expert at sitting in the stream, and it's sad if we don't have the chance to learn. That's the trouble with our bodies, our well-being, our health, it's all a muddle, even more of a muddle than what goes on in our heads, the chemistry and malign and benign things, glands and disorders. They say, why these mountains, why this disorder, why brave hostilities. I say, why ... but it doesn't matter what I say, it mustn't matter at all.

It mustn't! and she glares, this woman with the poker-back and the long brown, elegant skirt, very hard for a moment, into the sun.

Then one needs stiffening.

It starts with a little foreign cough, a dear little cough, rather dry, and people call you names, hypochondriac, and then suddenly they look and look and want to pour beetroot juice down the gullet.

Laundry

The official observer says, well, one ought to be terribly sad, if one is to lose one's life; but he admitted to a mere feeling of disappointment. A sun was causing the rim of the mountain to glow, it was late, the dawn had been cold, if one isn't certain of a thing one has only to produce women, he adds, they brought two, his wife and his mother, they wanted identification, his mother was strong and didn't bat an eyelash, they made ready to shoot him; poor man, she said, at the last minute life can seem very delicious, and shrugged, as though he were a complete stranger, he stared at her, straight in the face, he knew his mama wouldn't by so much as a flicker recognise him, his mother was out of the same mould as he, they said to her, come, nearer, nearer, and she said grimly, with sarcasm, if I must. His thin wife stood beside her, his wife was from a different mould, she was less ingenious, she broke down, she howled, and shrieked. Ah, women! the soldiers grinned. Because they'd caught the right fellow they shot him. It wasn't his relations he was disappointed in, says the official observer, a feeling sometimes has no name. Women are there to betray us, that is their purpose, their function, like handkerchiefs to wipe our noses.

The Summer Child

The old woman folds her hands over her tummy, she looks out of her window, and she says, it is not forgotten, you have only to see the arrogance of the train officials, in the ticket offices, on the line, how they refuse to speak our language, pretend they don't know a word of it, when all the time they can, they have to, they take an examination in it, with that job, in a two-language country.

And there are people who were children in the days when we were forced to have schooling in a foreign language, when even private tuition was forbidden, people who can speak the dialect and can't write correctly at all, can't write! That has to be very pathetic. The feeling is still not far beneath, and the arrogance of the officials on the railway is, for you, she says to the odd ill woman with the ram-rod back, like a glimpse into how it was for us.

They take our water, she says, they dam our water for their hydro-electric works, they drown villages and leave mocking church towers sticking up out of the middle, they used to mine our minerals and have abandoned them, they exploit nature, they take our timber, much of our timber disappears to the south. They pranced, once, they pranced in the country that was simply handed to them. It was hard.

A child went to school in those days and learnt nothing. It would come home and the mother would say, what have you been learning today? and the child would say, we learnt a kilosack. And the mother would say to the father, what is a kilosack? A kilosack? What does the child mean? The mother would question the child and be none the wiser. How could one guess? In the classroom the teacher would say, chi lo sa? chi lo sa? And the poor child would understand, kilosack. Ignorant, confused child, uneducated grown-up. Frightful! In our village for schoolteacher we had a Sicilian, and she was nice, she was good, and it was hard for her too. She would invite the teacher, the proper teacher, who had lost his position, she'd invite him in, which was courteous and intelligent of her. All our teachers lost their positions.

It was better when we were allowed to have private lessons, before that there was secret, underground tuition, and after the second war we had our own language in the schools again. It has been fairer, we have autonomy, we have arrangements.

But the ceiling? There are so many ceilings, precious things. Our culture. We suffered enough in two wars. The ceiling was an excuse. A last straw for some hot-heads. There are hot-heads everywhere. Or maybe it was a confusion, a kilosack.

And what hope for the wider world, with its atom weapons, if we tussle over a ceiling?

The girls once, she says, were content to wear the traditional garments of their own village, and live companionably together, without giving cause for envy. They start to see that those of a neighbouring district are prettier, so a few take to flaunting something different, now they all do, prettiness is more important to them, and the tourists do as well. The feeling of belonging to the country, if not the village, is strong enough. That isn't romantic, it's much deeper, is stronger indeed than the person, it is the tree and the person is the mistletoe, growing where it can. I expect the mistletoe too thinks, I am a pine tree, I am an oak, I am an apple tree, I don't suppose the mistletoe knows any better.

The melancholy I got from my father, she says.

I was forty when I married, one's first duty is to the

parents, and my father lived to eighty-four, his mind slipped towards the end. I was the only one left to care for them, though we were seven, my brother, who was a professor at the gymnasium, was hit on his bicycle by a car, killed on the road. My husband was eighteen years younger than I. We were very happy. The parish priest had wanted him to marry a niece of his own. But we were so happy. He had liver cancer. I sat by his bed at the hospital for five weeks, I rested my head on my hand, my elbow on his pillow, I slept for five weeks on my hand, with my legs always dangling down. And he asked if he could come home to die, we brought him in the ambulance, he couldn't have the drip any more, I had to give him injections, I could do that, he died quite quickly upstairs. I was ill, I was terribly ill, my legs were ill from sitting and dangling, they burst open, my lungs were full of water, they had to be drained, I lay in the convent hospital for seven weeks myself, they couldn't heal my legs, the pain was terrible. They couldn't heal my wounds, at last a herb doctor, a nature curer, gave me ointment, pig fat, I could suddenly bear to dig in the garden, I could press down on the spade with my foot, the wound covered itself with skin! He is not our real son, he is adopted, with forty it was too late for me.

He was our summer child, unexpected, un-looked for, his mother left him in a home and we had the telephone for the first time, a friend of my husband's, a priest, telephoned and asked if we would take the child. He was three and a half, and so thin, his cheeks furrowed, tears in his face, he was streaked with old tears.

And that was wonderful, wonderful, my husband was a teacher like my father, and then we wanted to adopt him, we had to find the mother, we found the grandparents, and we found the mother, it was agreed, she was content, and we had our summer child.

And now that gentle child is surrounded by soldiers.

There is so much traffic with foreigners. It is wrong. He is twenty nine. To have a summer child is beautiful. These days people live together, and separate. I find that hideous. Hideous.

I think we've understood each other well? she says, patting her tummy, as if after a good meal.

They are lovely in their own country, they should have stayed in it. A kilosack! she says. They didn't treasure our culture as they do their own, they tried to make us neglectful.

The Horse-Angel

But that isn't original, the child of twelve remarks, nothing is! I read a play, I think it was by William Shakespeare. Two old Welshmen are talking. And one says to the other, is beauty good. The other says, Beauty? I had her as a foal. Her dam was dead, and I reared the youngster on the bottle, no simple task with horses, and she possessed from the start a sunny temperament, I treated her with love, and she paid me with years of faithful work, never a harsh word between us, she was so willing, her nature was to trust and to try, she couldn't be mean, she put her shining shoulder into all I wanted of her until the day she herself went to heaven. If you ask me, is Beauty good, with all my heart I answer, Beauty was exceedingly good. A lovely dark brown, and silk feathers. A soft eye. And the one says, the child goes on, I was acquainted with a fellow who named his horse Desperation. For years he was mounting Desperation. I think it was, says the child, by Shakespeare.

Lichens

And one supposes that once one has reached the favourite spot, the place one loves and dreams of, one will be content to die; but it's the last thing one wants to do; in this loved place one is bursting with well-being, and looking ahead; no, to die one should go like a fox into a drain, and lie quietly in the dark, waiting for depression to overwhelm one.

I try to get rid of myself, she thinks, quite hard, and my unconscious exerts itself to protect me, to save and care for me. That's comic! I arrive. I arrive, and remember that I've asked to witness my will someone who'll be upset if it comes too soon into operation, so my hands are tied, it is all most convenient. The unconscious should have taken me to the bank, where the officials are less tender, positively insensitive. I can do no more than greet the favoured spot with a wry smile, and turn back. I am not professional enough. Kleist was a professional, she thinks, suicide.

But I risk a stray bullet in the fighting. I am drawn to stray bullets, or a slip in the melting snowfields. She cheers up.

I still try to pin names to flowers, to mountains, to insects and birds. Some day their names won't matter, one will long simply for mountains, to see flowers, watch humming insects and birds. There won't be any stray bullets, and I shall notice the drain. In heaven the flowers have no names. One will be quite lost. Familiarity is all. Among unknown peaks one is at sea, at home only when one's eye rests on old friends.

I spend hours communing with nature, she thinks, but where does it get me, nature answers, and in a voice nobody else can hear, it is a perfectly hermetic discussion. I would rather spend hours with nature than with anyone else. Almost anyone else.

And if with one body talking without opening our mouths were to be possible, if thoughts were to flit like bats between us, flit, flit, to and fro, as animals speak; if that were to be possible; and if nature were to hear us, what then?

A grand passion is easy, as easy as flying off the handle. It's a subtler thing, infinitely, one thinks of, which confirms our equilibrium, would confirm it.

Haven't we been abandoned by the means of communication? We have language, we waggle our tongues, but no speech. And occasionally one comes across such an animal. What that animal says is misinterpreted by his fellows, he can't make himself understood aright, and so he gets a reaction he hasn't anticipated, and is bewildered. That's a pathetic phenomenon. It must be similar to the state of human beings.

Art can speak to us, Beethoven and Hölderlin speak to us out of a great distance, to some even a god speaks.

If one is high in the mountains, one can appear absentminded, one can sit out in the cold, I imagine, at night, one becomes sleepy. That speaks of grace. To cast oneself into the tail of a glacier, so as to emerge, in time-lapse, intact, dead but intact, at the snout, speaks of less grace, it requires self-possession, perhaps. I can't describe the innards of glaciers, she thinks.

One is progressively losing one's drift, one is growing blurred, one's science deserts one, as a glacier moves. One will be helpless among the unnamed and the unnameable, rock and snake, water. Yet our feelings cry out to be small and sharp. So we collect stuff to render them neutral, those feelings, local. Otherwise they would kill us, send us to kill ourselves. I carry a tobacco tin into which to stick my petrified or dormant deaths;

stones, fossils, seeds; and lichens, by which one can tell how high one is on the mountain.

If one looks, with an uneducated eye, at lichens, she says, they can seem to reflect the world, one finds antlers, and stars, flowers, silver grey or dark grey, and green, it is as if grey has never been so mysterious. But they need other lives to live on, they need friends.

I suppose, she says, in her gloomy, lichen-coloured mood, though even in lichen there is a thing that shines, one could carry a picnic out into the snow, and shoot a little bird for one's friend. A friend on whose existence one too can be a parasite. It must be better to cling than to wallow.

And to have, in the end, one's hand kissed by an idiot, nicely, a cockerel-crowing, owl-hooting idiot, a simpleton! After so much wanting, she thinks, to be kissed and kiss, a lifetime of it.

It comes at one like an idiot, like a child, in impetuous fragments, torn and twisted, and we have to spend so much of it trying to make sense of it, order out of the confusion, such a waste of effort on life's part.

Lichen can't be a parasite, one can't be a parasite on a stone.

I dream. I dreamt, she says, of being in a bed with a large boxer; of ghosts, stalking past, a tall grim man and his acolytes, a procession; of the dog's trembling, his shaking all over; of my trembling; and of the comfort of knowing the ghosts were visible to Oskar, the dog.

She brushes a cobweb from her face. One sees those medieval wheels of life, or is it death, with people clinging on as they turn, babes at one o'clock, portly at three, and becoming ashen-haired by six, in middle age, doddery at nine, skeletal at eleven, one imagines the wheel is hauling its creatures round, but no, they cling to it, sometimes they have handles, and it is they that tug and throw their puny weight against the wheel, making it turn, slowly, slowly. Without people and their clinging, upsetting its balance, the wheel would stay motionless.

You've got it all wrong, the little bird says, it's Death who pulls on the handle.

Soldiering On

I feel stifled, he says, I feel stifled in the city, and I come higher, I feel stifled still, I go higher up on the mountain, where the air ought to be crisp and fresh, and I feel stifled, I feel stifled all the time, high on the mountain the weather is lowering and heavy, the wind blows from the south, that sickening, bad-weather wind, and I so want to feel not stifled for a moment. But one should have one's heart broken by the weather, that is what weather is for; and the mountains must seem sullen and cold.

If beauty has a purpose, she is there for us to spoil. It is given to us to walk and look at the litter, we can watch the paper handkerchiefs slowly disintegrating, plastering themselves over heather, myrtle and stone, we can calculate from which perfect spot a yoghurt pot has been thrown, there are plenty of yoghurt pots in the mountains, no dearth, we can perch on seats that are not for bottoms to sit on by the paths leading from villages to the forest but to have cigarette ends strewn around them, bottles tucked under them, and to invite in the manner of tit-boxes futile nests to be laid with half-roasted tins in colonies nearby. It does us good, to see the flowers become fewer. Because we have to learn to take leave of it. I am curious, I force myself on, I'd burst a blood vessel to peep over the next ridge, and the next, to be, yes, to be, not merely stand, by a remote and lovely lake, to clamber on. I need to be able to say, that I shall never now see, there I shall never be, or stand. And, I am content. I don't try to imagine it. I don't send my mind ahead of me, like a hound. I keep it to heel, in the muck. I am tired. I admit, I am tired. One has to cease being so eager. One has to say, I shall never see the alpenrose in bloom again. I shall never lie down with gentians. I shan't scent the pine resin quite so keenly as one does high above the rest of the earth. One has to say, at least I am a little acquainted, I know how it could be, I've had a glimpse. I didn't dream it, it was true.

If once upon a time man rejoiced in his oneness with nature, these days he must learn to feel alienated. How else can we bear what it is we shall have to put up with in the way of change. But what we feel, or think we feel, when we set eyes on a spruce tree with blue flowers, the clematis sprawling over little spruces, or when the meadows begin to warm themselves after the rain, and the mountains glitter with snow in the light that shines following a storm, when we see cyclamen, wild and high, so high, where it's frosty and bitter, and cushions of violet-red saxifrage smelling of honey, what we feel is the faintest vestige, of that oneness with nature.

There is a new world for people who shit in cattle mangers, he says, Walther says, leaning on his stick, who know no better. What does a cow think, or a farmer, who finds human shit topped with pink flags of lavatory paper in the wooden place where cattle put their mouths, in every byre of every alm. Are these the folk that take the bells from necks which are intended to ring during munching and swallowing? Are they the folk who stuff their beer-cans in all the crannies, all the crevices in the rock? See how the unfortunate flowers in the track of the tourists vanish, how those in a sister valley remain a moment longer, not yet uprooted. But flowers are there to have their little heads trampled upon and their feet whipped from under them, we should direct the strange people, who fail to greet each other, pretend fellow creatures see right through fellow creatures, to the more secret valleys, they'd make splendid use of them, such people don't waste their time. He looks through his binoculars, army exercises! he says with derision, his hand trembling.

The roar of a distant, tiny avalanche, the uncanny thud of a stone dropping, it is all there for us not to hear again, one shouldn't ever have a valley to oneself, a small, smooth and indeed secret valley, and a stream where the pebbles flash, green with copper, and white and red and grey, in the water, and large creamy anemones stand in the snow, it is all ripe for spoiling, for besmirching, and a rainbow, arching his back over the mountainside, hugging it, low and close, colouring the trees and turf with fairy shades, those too, I am sure we can spoil rainbows.

One has to check oneself, to say one doesn't care so much about this spot and that, it doesn't mean so much, things don't, life doesn't, one has to keep oneself in check. He brings his binoculars to the eye and stares incredulously. There are people for whom life is so unbearable they have to kill themselves, one should spare a thought for them, as one soldiers on.

Hands

The bees can't go to the alm, the driver says, they want to, they tell me they would like to go to the alm as they always do, they are accustomed to going in June, then they come home in September, one has to get up at four to take them, when they're all present, and they're dopey from a night's sleep, one can take them up there, and they can be happy and spend their summer, they can be busy, they have much to do, the alm is heaven for bees, and it does them good, it's terrible to have bees telling one they want to go to the alm, and having to deny them their little pleasure, bees have small pleasures, and they chatter to each other, they'll have less to talk about, my father was cleverer than I at explaining things to bees, my father used to carry the bees on his back.

Bees have no hands, the passenger behind him says, they must be grateful to be carried for a change. I wonder how we'd cope without them. Hands write, and play music, there are virgin hands on priests, and rougher hands that work. I don't know how you can drive, she says, in her reedy, inconsequential voice, with so much on yours. She is well, evidently, acquainted with him.

I have a great deal of time, he says.

Your hands aren't the hands of a poet, she says, you have earth ingrained. Poets' hands are white and beautiful.

Oh, rubbish, exclaims another passenger, who sits behind the passenger behind the driver, it is nice to see earth engrained, why should poets have white hands?

It's shocking, to see his hands! the old lady says. They speak to the back of each other's heads, so they bellow to be heard and understood above the engine.

Your poet, the passenger behind her says, has an alabaster brow with a lock of black hair dangling on it, burning eyes, and velvet trousers.

The old lady says, yes, agreeably surprised.

I am a peasant, the driver says.

The old lady would like to allow herself to snort.

I scythe tomorrow, he remarks, to his cartload of women with bags, all day tomorrow for me, and the next day for my neighbour, and the day after that I drive the omnibus. The hay is late, perhaps by four weeks. The ground is packed, first with inches of rain, and now with drying wind, and we have had less sunshine than we expect at this season, the grass is weakened, there isn't the thickness in the bottom.

The driver whistles, partly Bach, partly a variation of his own.

They have their hay below, someone farther behind him calls.

They are warmer, of course, the old lady says.

Our grass is harder, he says, the higher the grass grows, has to grow, the harder the variety, their grass is quite different.

And what of the poisonous stuff?

The yellow? That is good, when it's cut and dries, the poison goes out of it, we say. The herbs are all good, our hay is the most nourishing, if I were a cow I'd rather live on my hay than theirs for the winter, we have luck in certain respects and our cattle too. But we can mow only twice, they below mow thrice.

And the red? That passenger looks at it from her window.

The sorrel, also good, he says. He takes a swing at a bend in the very narrow road.

So without hands we couldn't carry the bees or scythe or pick our apples, or milk, he says grinning, we couldn't change a wheel, when one changes a wheel oneself it is satisfying, but to sit in the empty road, one's feet in an overgrown ditch, watching another driver with a wheel to change, even if one isn't keen to be in either spot, on or back, and there are summer flowers on the bank, that is queer! One stares at that wheel with impatience. A well-known poem, he says, with a little decoration.

By Goethe?

Not by Goethe, he says. Goethe didn't live in the days of motors. By Brecht.

Your fingernails! the old passenger says.

What a to-do! the other passenger says. Hands are made in the likeness of roots, so we can plunge them into the earth.

And to write, poems, to paint, pictures, the old lady says stubbornly, to draw, to hold a bow, to play the piano. What else, she says vaguely. I forget.

It can't be earth that prevents one.

If a hand is bigger than its fellow, through having been plunged in the earth as an onion is, bigger and clumsier notes must be heard from that hand.

What onion is plunged in the earth? You talk nonsense, the much younger passenger says rather rudely.

And the thorns? The thorns under the nail render it all more poignant, I suppose? the driver asks.

I'm no friend to onions, he adds.

He pulls up by the lychgate, was it at this spot you wished to be set down, dear, he says. The old lady tussles with her basket. The engine thuds and pants. Five others blunder out and go their separate ways.

They should make me a gravestone of pumice, he says.

The passenger still sitting two seats behind him says, one is never finished, there is always something else, to haunt one's stomach and eat one's mind up.

If the bees could understand the meaning of gunfire, he says . . . He brakes for a mouse.

For us, isn't silence better? she says. Why else are we

blessed with mouths that shut and lips that can close on everything inside? And teeth which will bite on chagrin.

It's our hands, I fear, not our voices, he says, which have made a mess of the sweet air.

Poor bees, she says.

There will be bitter gall swimming in the honey, he says. They laugh. He grips the wheel, tighter.

We laugh! We should be ashamed.

The Insatiable Wheel

The third child, says the peasant in broad dialect, has a little tricycle, a toy thing for very small children, and he goes pedalling off on it, for miles and miles, at the age of three, when no one is looking, he has the urge to pedal miles, to the mountains, at the age of three, on a baby's tricycle; and the old dog always goes with him; I meet him miles from home, pedalling along like a fury, and the dog running alongside, he slips out when no one is looking, and the dog like his shadow, people say she protects him, has it in her head to protect him, I don't know so much; and I meet him out in the country and I call to him, Franzi, was machst du hier?, wohin?, and he smiles radiantly, not naughtily or guiltily, and says in his baby voice, bicycling, to the mountains he says, and the old dog too; and I try to explain it's dangerous, he's too young to be out in the country miles from home alone, and he smiles, and smiles, and there's no stopping him; it's my wheel, he says, my wheel is hungry, it eats and I can't stop it, it's terribly hungry, me and the dog takes it out to eat; and he waves to me, cheerfully he waves to me, a three-year-old, and off he pedals, his little knees hitting his chin, and the hair busy in the wind, and his baby arms poised on the rotten little handlebars as if he was in a race, puffing and serious, and the dog's flanks thin and shadowy beside him, the dog not saying a thing to me; and I call, come with me, Franzi, you and the dog can have a lift with me; and he says, don't forget the boy's Radl, his little tricycle, his insatiable wheel, don't forget his Radl; he means himself, the boy; how do you keep a child in? I say to his big brother, can't you keep an eye on Franzi, it's dangerous for him to be eaten up by his Radl, and we are all helpless, the child slips away, when no one's looking, he picks his time, what will a child do when he's grown up, that slips off to the mountains on a tiny tricycle, so strong and wilful a baby, insatiable; don't forget my Radl whatever you do, he says, don't leave my Radl here in the road, miles from home, and he smiles with total innocence, total guile.

I fall awake and think, I want to go home. But there is no home. I have been dreaming of furniture again, two sticks of furniture and a hen-house. The last two sticks. I pat and stroke my furniture. The oak gleams, that is the only reply, the hindmost passenger, the expert on ceilings and baroque plaster, says.

I think, it doesn't matter where I am, whether calm or with nerves shot to pieces, in the mountains, in towns, sleeping well or sleeping badly, it doesn't matter, I am quite lost, wherever I am. I want to surrender. I wish to retire. I am tired. I'm not disappointed, but I can't cast my mind any farther, I'd prefer to draw it in and keep it in a bag.

I don't belong in these mountains, in any mountains, I am straying. I hold out my arms all night. To whom? and what for? Let me have a garden, let me have a dog, let me have privacy. There was once a garden, there have been gardens, full of privacy, I must have been born to a large estate.

When I was a child I thought there was a shrub called privy, a fellow came to clip the privy, honeysuckle concealed the privy, in the privy's brown and twiggy parts I hid and spiders lived, privy was a place for easing nature, I knew that to be a truth, privy grew so happily the fellow had to curb it.

I'd like a garden to be privily shrouded sometimes in white, at dusk, with ground clouds, as the heaven of my childhood, she says gruffly, was in nightmares. Deep in the hummocks of the orchard I'd lie down, and hear the larks, all proper gardens have orchards, all proper orchards have hummocks, nature could ease herself with willows, dykes, dragonflies, and shadows, many fruits, many flowers, many, and toads, old-fashioned gardens had frogs, all gardens should have nettle beds and bramble beds, reed mace, meadowsweet, and swallows, there should always be swallows in the summer, they bring one their news, and swifts to scream, a linden, and of all the trees one tree to be aloft in, I may seem lumbering and my leg gammy but I'm nimble, a tree with copper leaves, I think, and tiger-moth caterpillars, whose appetite needn't be voracious, in a high wind one can feel the trunk flex, flex and stir, against one's spine, one can, from such a tree, watch duck slip past in the water, wild duck, that peculiar expression on their faces they have when they believe themselves alone. I want to be invisible. I was born in the mud month, sōl-mōnath, I relish mud, scum and squelch. I want to be invisible. I have too much presence, I can't imagine why, and I'd like to throw it away, not for a moment as a wild animal does, no, for ever. A garden is terribly companionable. In a marsh one can disappear and be brushed by things, I could be patted, I could be touched and stroked by plants, plants have a gift for it, they have the quietest hands, only when one is alone with plants do they choose to touch and stroke one, they reach out. But my old friend stirs inside its trunk still, it has to, in a high wind. No doubt there is the smell of growing and germinating. No doubt there is water in the dyke, no doubt there are snipe, and duck with rapt faces, no doubt the trees, the natives and the trees from abroad, have put on inches, no doubt, and in the snow, when it snows, the stoat will leave footprints. Better never to have known it, if that was what beauty was, to have to hanker after it.

I wonder if senility is like that, suffering glimpses.

Duck can be chucked out of gardens, she says, if they exceed their nature and stray, but when a creature is tame, and wild though we feed it, territory is awkward for it, the innocent are unruly, it isn't any use being sentimental, if a maverick duck, not a mallard, a pet, tastes every morsel and tramples, with her webbed feet, in the flowers, if she encroaches, as weeds in a marsh, hogweed, bindweed and nettles, encroach on the orchids, if she makes a general nuisance of herself, a trap will be set with almond slice and sprung and goodbye duck, banished, to swim or sink in a far pond.

I wonder if she lives.

The trouble with plaster, she says, a grizzled, cropped person, is that it can't be precisely restored.

But we invest the silly stuff with too much meaning. Plaster ought to have limitations, yet if one stares hard at that angel, one notices a hand has told those grains to live together, a hand has worked a pink and blue angel out of dust, out of sand, out of lime, and hidden in the body will be the hair of beasts, some hands are good at having words with angels, some hands poor, many awful, one can only make now a little memory, a dear little memory, she treasures the dialect, and the hand that originally made the angel didn't tell him to speak, merely made an angel, in the days before motors when proper angels had neither one sex nor the other, an angel, according to his lights, to us he speaks, so we must make an angel that speaks, which is complicated, someone once patted and stroked the plaster, we touch infant plaster and entreat it to seem old.

I used to wonder, how soon do the seagulls, flying over, see the sea?

That hindmost passenger then stops thinking, it was the last kick from an unconscious horse.

The alpenrose is beginning to bloom, the mouse cows and the red are ringing their bells, the sky is wide open, sun pours onto the mountains, goats are running through the snowfields, somewhere there are glaciers and they are moving. The breeze hums.

PEACOCK ISLAND

Daffodils

If she kicks the bucket, I am to plant daffodils on her grave, she won't forget, she doesn't forgive, I laughed unkindly, yet I was chiefly to blame, I bought a net of daffodil bulbs and dropped them in the vegetable rack, she came along and cut them up as onions, took the peel off and cooked them, fairly whole, with potatoes, when they were done she realised she'd taken my daffodil bulbs, why one realises bulbs aren't onions once they're cooked and misses it while they're raw I've no idea, perhaps daffodils make one cry, she and her friend, the one who'd come to a bite of food, the woman that wears purple cardigans, two at a time, they thought it silly to waste the potatoes, they told each other it would be all right if they scooped out the daffodils, so they ate up the potatoes cooked with daffodils and were violently, without time to reach a telephone, paralytically, ill, on the floor, they writhed on the floor and were rescued by the baker's son, a brave fellow of fifteen, he called an ambulance, they just made it, they managed to live, and suppose the baker didn't deliver and at half-past one! Or is it onions on her grave. The tears arrive in her eyes. I think, she goes through life with an arm held up to shield her, in front of her face, to ward off the blows, that's how not to notice daffodils aren't onions? The tears come out of her eyes and wobble down her cheeks, at long last she smiles. And what if the baker's boy, seeing two women, writhing women, on the floor, one in two purple cardigans, as he peered politely through the kitchen window and waited, what if he'd popped the bread on the threshold and bolted for dear life, who could have blamed him, I at fifteen, seeing two women on the floor, writhing or not, would have bolted, he had the presence of mind to turn the handle and, finding both women speechless, long past being able to mouth anything but saliva and foam, use our telephone, I hate the telephone, I've always hated it, the potatoes in daffodil juice were still steaming on the table, fortunate indeed the baker's son connected steaming plates to women on the floor, those poor plates she wanted to chuck away, I'd washed them up while they were sitting around and we couldn't tell the daffodil plates from all the others of the same pattern, she wanted to throw all the plates away, not in the dustbin, she thought of burying them in the garden, there are shards in plenty in the soil already, I often meet them, perhaps their owners ate daffodils too, perhaps the house has a legend of daffodil-eating, I'm surprised we didn't have to uproot every daffodil, the pretty little wild ones and all the fancy jobs, and the narcissi, we didn't do that. If she was so distracted with woes as not to notice daffodils weren't onions, better not to confide in people with purple cardigans, in the hot months the purple cardigans are reduced by half and an unsuitable vest is worn beneath, lower down one has no eyes for, it's all much of a muchness.

The old girl has woes, women tend to have woes and dwell on them, they bear grudges like apple blossom, if I'd been the son of that baker I'd have borne a grudge, but I believe he's a sea scout, he's trained to cope, he was capable of letting the hospital doctors know that daffodils were the problem, I can't imagine how he could be so wise, he was a mere fifteen at the time. The bread order wasn't increased.

Women have woes because men come along and by leaving daffodil bulbs in the vegetable rack dare them to be so stupid, and because men all their lives might mistake daffodils bulbs for onions and somehow don't, she says women can't escape, they're confronted with onions. I am the very fellow most likely to mistake daffodils for onions, I might have writhed violently ill on the floor underneath my steaming plate, no woman in her senses would make such a slip-up, but by virtue of being a woman she's fated to spend much of her time slightly adrift, not in her senses, out of them, I can't imagine why the friend with purple cardigans was being entertained to potatoes and onions, did they desire nothing else? Of all women I'd have taken that one for a good trencherman.

If a daffodil could be pink and white, she could be a daffodil, her face has a very sad expression on it, I catch it when she's in repose, her mouth at the corners droops, or it opens, the lips are parted, as if some terrible cry is escaping, they're silent, those lips, the corners of her eyes droop, lines fan over her cheekbones, it isn't ugly, it's rather wonderful. We most of us see daffodils as smiling, the colour of the sun, they're crying, they have bulbs, what's more, hidden in darkness that poison, we all do, it seems I though no daffodil have a dormant poison that sends sly white things into my earth, my bulb has a spring strength, we human beings are a crowd of naughty bulbs. I expect if one enquired, she wouldn't have been thinking especially, I don't suppose she'd be lying, expressions are funny, they show so much, more than we know, and in the same moment even they're whispering I can't, I can't say it, I'm not aware of it, it wells from a depth, and, thank goodness, one might hear her add, if that's how you describe it, an uglier emotion doesn't well, she mustn't fear, it's not a mean, small look, although disturbing, I have no notion of what brings it to her face, if she could see herself she'd be surprised. I may be oblivious to her woes, she may be right. One has no business to demand that all one's minor anguishes be acknowledged. A daffodil seems to smile an uncompli-cated smile and beg only that it not be stepped on, daffodils do suffer injury nevertheless, with that bulb full of poison how could it do them any real harm, I'd fall over rather than make a daffodil writhe. Domestic slavery, a life bound up with onions and tears, and having no money of their own, because of hands so reeking of onions, puts those expressions on women's faces, the old girl retorts, that doesn't explain to me why hers is the face of a daffodil and the purple cardigan has a broad bean's.

And smiling, or cut and still smiling, daffodils foam at their wounds, their saliva runs over one's hands, would they prefer to be stepped on or to be cut, the smile when crushed at least lingers, bravely they smile on, with torn eyes and mouths, it is odd that women are adept at cutting flowers and feel no pangs, and foam at their wounds, if one is stepped on and cut one would, it can be imagined, grow club feet, yet neither does that, the face never loses its painful charm, and it smiles, and smiles, the daffodils in the garden may be screaming but they keep their lovely faces.

Frothing at their wounds, they dip their hands in the washing-up, blazing they shatter plates and bury shards in the garden, and, prosaic, practical, scorn sentiment, one can't afford sentiment when one is condemned to look lovely though torn at the mouth and eyes, trampled and ignored, so many of them that waves of them smile and scream and do this inexorable duty with hoovers and egg-boiling and taking the spines out of sardines, and far worse, only if one wears purple cardigans two at a time can one look blunted, a hybrid, that has lost its scent, has lost the gift of smiling through her tears.

The old girl's angry, because I mock, she fills flower vases with onions, they sit all over the house, and spring flowers lie without water, suffering, in the vegetable rack, and we shall never be allowed to forget it, those in the garden likewise are forced to sway with the storms, look lovely, fade, grow old gracefully, be trampled. Oh, oh! commiserates the purple cardigan, who should have had, too, more sense. At the hospital they were kind, in hospitals they know only of cut flowers.

Hands in onion bags, lives permanently interrupted, they have to accustom themselves to feeling the less-loved, less-favoured, of nature's creatures, like a less-loved child.

I still have things to tell Florus. I dreamt of losing a dog, it was not he, I was accompanied by three dogs, or four, we were walking in deep woods along the flank of a hill, with wild roses in flower, the dogs plunged upwards and down, crossed my path continually, and soon the oldest wasn't with us, we'd lost her, tunnels ran below our feet, stone workings, blackness appeared if one parted the bracken, steam slipped from fissures, we re-traced our steps, the other dogs and I, we called, we searched, they looked, they turned their heads, I called and called and whistled, they listened, we tramped to exhaustion, we went home, I came out alone and repeated all that, I went home, I came out and bumped into a fellow who claimed he'd seen a person with a dog, from his description I thought the old dog had been stolen, had consented to climb into a motor car and be driven away, until I realised the man had seen me, with a dog which resembled her, but it was not the old girl, for an hour my heart was in my mouth, I went home, I dozed, I came out, I found her by a hayrick, halfway on her road home, she had miles to walk, her pads were sore, we cried to see each other and didn't say much. I still have things to tell Florus. I dream often of that long hillside, those wild roses, dog roses.

I don't know what would have been in her mind as she rested by the hayrick, when she set eyes on me there was no greeting in her face, great relief was written all over her body, I don't know what she'd have thought, realising herself lost and then left, she would have run to and fro, several miles through the woods, looking for us, confused by our scent, with alarm and anxiety, before deciding to start for home, I don't know exactly how instinct relates in which direction home is, or what would have gone through her head, or if she'd walked behind the hedges or along the verge, or what had defended her against curious passers-by, or how she'd come to be beside the hayrick, if she'd crawled under the gate or climbed the wall, what she imagined I'd done, what thoughts do run through the mind of a dog alone, what seriousness is brought to tackle the problem, what mixture of reasoning and instinct, or how she would have arrived home, and when, I know she would have arrived home totally without rancour. A conspicuous dog, she lay under a hayrick, watchful, but remote, dreamy, making herself very inconspicuous indeed, near dusk I found her. It's unbearable, still.

I've been putting meals down on the floor for people for more than half my life, perhaps for most of it, that looses some soothing juice in one's own stomach, feeding animals has a sensation attached, similar to having one's hair stroked. The smells of their food, raw and its cooking, paunch, sheep's head, raw and cooked flesh, I have them in my nostrils until I drop, even the act of bending to place dishes on stools, it's burnt into me, food on the floor or on stools according to whom, or what, one is feeding, the length of leg. Florus was a delicate eater, though not fussy. I need to lay meals down for people on the floor and feel that my hair has been stroked. It's instinct, as breaking the ice on the horses' water has to become if one is never to forget it. Florus may be waiting to be fed, I don't know, trying to understand, with a mixture of reasoning and instinct. I'd always thought, it must be a nightmare to have horses nowadays, when horses disappear overnight from their fields and one scours the countryside for months, one's stomach in one's mouth, churning.

An old dog becomes wrapt up in its aging, but Florus was companionable, he wouldn't pass without a smile, we didn't pass each other in the house or garden without by some flicker saying something, a smile, an answer, one can't tell him all that is in one's mind, it isn't physically possible, one can leave the mind ajar, not shut him out, only when need be, Florus picked up much of what I thought, he has a leg in the human world and a leg with animals.

I miss Florus in the garden and in the house. I miss Florus.

It can be very poignant, the absence, and the longing.

Almost a year. To the week.

Florus sighs, and sings, and moans, and holds my wrist in his teeth, draws me by the wrist, the arm, into the garden, his eyes fixed on my face. He sighs from pleasure, in pain he is painfully silent, one hears a contained silence, perhaps not unlike the silence of the old dog in the lee of her hayrick. Florus grunts, with the pretended exertion of taking me by the wrist into the garden.

I was curious to know exactly how he saw and smelt the garden. I tracked him, trying to understand. He tries hard enough, after all, to understand me. Without a nose I was bound to feel half of it was lost to me. I could recognise fox, badger, rabbit, mouse, and fowls, horse, pig, one or two human beings hot, I like being able to identify the individual scent of human beings, one can in that moment, when they sweat, how do flowers smell to Florus? Did he smell flowers? In the early morning the garden is shining with wet gossamer, I and he both breast it, Florus sinks into the grass, or he touches poppies with his lips, a sensuous thing, to watch a dog touch poppy petals with his lips, a shrew hurries through the long grass, Florus sticks his nose into the mat, and breathes fire, and again farther on, and again, all across the manure on the rhubarb bed walk his four paws, the sun hangs red in the eastern corner, the shrubs touch us, we brush damp twigs, if it snows in the winter there are footprints, the dogs roll in the snow, perhaps crushing what's underneath, yet perhaps not, they snuffle the snow and let their jaws dangle. I was sure Florus loved me. And one supposes a dog trusts one to look after him, her. At the last oak one can stand and survey the fields where the midges dance, Florus and I stand there, separately, together, a stoat lives in a rotten willow stump, it is summer and winter and spring and every garden I have ever half possessed. Florus is sure, somewhere, I love him and will look after him. I am helpless.

One's instinct is set alight, homing instincts are of all kinds and natures. Or nature's. I expect he loved the garden. I expect the garden misses him. I expect. Helpless.

He sits by me while I weed, he thrusts his nose into the earth, he picks up weeds, shakes them, throws them over his shoulder, Florus examines plants, nudging them, he wants to know what it is I do to the plants with my hands, I show him things, he picks blackberries beside me, he drifts away, in earshot, out of earshot, if I step round the garden he follows me, a few reticent paces behind, happy to keep me company, and because he's partial to mine; sometimes he leans against me, silent. I saw firewood, he is close, an absent expression on his face, or he drags a branch across the grass, his body bent like a bow, he's strong enough to pull a branch whilst heading forwards, not backwards, he may have been stronger than I. His face would change, as emotion transforms one, when a smoothing or a wrinkling occurred in his thoughts.

Florus could boil and blow up, he had spirit, he could settle, and go very sweetly, he is more horse than hound. I used to think so. In clashes of will I drew myself up, my whole self together, and sent my authority, my expectation, into the air, as unseen and as felt as the growing of plants, fruits and seeds, one learns to cast one's authority from living with horses, not dogs, with horses one doesn't win, one expects and admires with every particle, even with one's fingers one expresses that, how one holds one's body, one's eyes, how one holds one's mind, and, being so open, one has the ability to hide half of oneself, to shut down, it's a trick, never to be abused. I can push Florus, I think, not lead him. Or I'd leave him alone, let him drift away into a private dream.

He eyes me, he can cast his own self into the air, as stubborn as a falling tree, he knows how to shut his mind, and to him it's second nature, I'd like access to my second nature, I fumble, I know no more than what I've learnt.

The breeze flows over his face, raises his ears, there are apples in the trees, or primroses in the lane, deep mud on the path, a wall of snow, ice, fish, a platoon of brown fish swims past in the water, it is early in the summer, a magpie's carcass hides in the long grass, purple with dew, swans creak above us, we look, and look. Florus isn't thinking of me at all, he runs over the fields, he is with me and he isn't, even if for a few strides he chooses to walk beside me, he is running in his mind over the fields, keen to miss nothing, it is a comfortable arrangement, he stares at the heron as she clambers into the sky, there are always rivers, water vole, there may be a hare, and indecipherable stains on swede tops, it's remarked upon, we share our curiosity about the world, it's remarked upon, he leaves me to my private dream, he doesn't intrude, he doesn't bother me, the snow falls and the trees are quiet, he shows me where an owl has slept, or dozed while hunting. I keep all these things now to myself, I have no choice.

Florus sighs, and sings, and moans, and holds my wrist in his teeth, and draws me by the wrist, the arm, into the garden, his eyes fixed on my face. He has things to tell me. The air is filled by flowers. I can do nothing to retrieve him, nothing. I wish he didn't think of me. I wish he'd appear at the door.

And he pulls me like a branch over the grass. I know what the branch feels, despairing.

I dreamt of the old dog, she was lost, I spotted her at the shore of a lake, she stared towards home, blindly, I was somehow the cause of it, she was stranded, the lake was huge, its water alight, wind-surfers staggered all over it, dinghies flew, white yachts, white sails, and red, a pretty ketch, and coloured spinnakers, naked people sat at their tillers, she moved with great purpose along the shore, she was looking anxious, I was torn, not a mile across the lake lay an island with rushy inlets and a peculiar white castle, a white fan-tail amongst the dark trees, and buildings that were half mock, half functional, bordered on insanity, though a pony grazed in a paddock and duck plopped in and out of the shallows, and oaks, oddly tall, cedars, rare trees, flowers and peafowl and fountains, she could have swum to the island, only a narrow channel on, from island to home, she couldn't swim, she never had been able to, she wouldn't strike out but remained on the lake fringe, she was pulled up short by a wire fence in the forest, and if she could have climbed it she would have come to, from my vantage point I noticed, a dull white wall, clear of woods, a wall which severed all the houses from their tranquil view, she re-traced her path, she was frightened yet concentrating on the problem, she was in the village, formerly a settlement of summer houses, she had to pass the jetties, she dodged and swerved from friendly hands, she looked at the ferry boats, she frowned, her mouth opened and her tongue was hanging out, she was panting, she drew her lips back at the corners. Her legs swung into a trot. She didn't rest, she moved along the shore, she would round the lake, it wasn't a lake, it was rather too far, it was a river, for a dog on her own, she knew she was heading away from home, her homing instinct tore her, if she was to save herself, she slipped from my sight, and I thought, she will never make it, I shan't see the poor girl again.

Shooting the Bolt

But we need a companion, it's a humiliating necessity, like a handle in the bath and the rubber mat. Olive says, she can't bear women, possibly she loathes them, she walks in streets and women walk ahead of her, quite unknown women, with their secret smells and their secrets, their understanding of what it is to be a woman, missing in her, she sees under their arms, into their armpits, up their legs, she smells their secret between-the-legs, good heavens, smells, these legs trot along, omniscient, in the perfect certainty they don't belong to a frog, they trot on heels, arm in arm, women's legs do, amusing themselves with complaints about men. How to be rid of her! Currant bushes don't put muck on their faces and their lips are already sweetly red, or black, or even lemon-white, she prefers currant bushes, and how they smell. The fruit cage floats blue in the morning mist, when watched from afar, its wire shimmers, I don't know how she came to be locked in, it's a mystery, and I'm thankful, when I noticed its floating, I wasn't even aware she was, let alone what she was thinking in it, I don't wish to be told. Olive is attached to the fruit cage, she spends hours on her hands and knees, weeding, or wading up to her armpits in the raspberry canes, raspberries remind her of horses' lips, soft fruit, apparently, is fierce and brave and stands up, she had only to wriggle her fingers through the wire of the old door, to reach the bolt, one isn't truly locked in the fruit cage, but how, she thought, do I get out of being a woman, it is repugnant, she lay down in the last of the dew, the currants slowly subsided in the colander. It seems women are three-quarters human being, they are hens, they teach each other, mother to daughter, how to be, sister to sister. The remaining quarter is a kind of gland that fills us with hennish emotion, we overflow, women are seldom contained, we seep, I seep, she seeps too, the frog had disappeared and she wondered if there was a hole in the fruit cage, it's become a nightmare, such an unsettling, scornful person to have in the house. Olive thought of wire and wire cutters, of the smell of galvanised wire, the smell of scratches from bending wire, galvanised blood, one shouldn't, she thought, be galvanised by such smells, and nowadays not by the smells of ironing and boiling jam either.

She is turning her will to the jam, it is already three rows deep on the pantry shelf, more than can possibly be eaten and bestowed, she can't let the crop go to waste, and why? It's nothing to do with her, really. I expect she'll insist on picking all the apples from their branches. A terrible, relentless will. And blinkered! Olive fastens on some task, at first imagines we'll be delighted, she finds we're not, and still does it, we don't bother with the fruit cage, why should she? I didn't realise having one was so ambiguous a venture. I can't enjoy our garden any longer, whenever I go out she's in it. A moral crusade is on, to pick all the fruit, and women, it seems, have a moral duty, to stand up like raspberries, it's not enough, never to have hurt a fly, people's private codes, I think, of conduct can be tiresome, unfortunately we got her and she has the effrontery to like it with us here.

A lark was singing, she squinted into the sky, women used to be rather unpleasant to other women, these days, struggling for what she's always taken for granted, yet endowed with what she doesn't have, they tend to be nice, is she jealous, oh no, it's we who are jealous of her blasted confidence, why doesn't she have chips on her shoulders, why is she so unnatural, why aren't her shoulders raw? Ranting and raving! I use a knife on wasps, she disapproves, as a child she had the job of constructing the wasp traps, jam and cider in a jar, dreadful, she says, her grandfather's wasp clippers, a family heirloom, were more humane, her grandfather who invented them could catch wasps on the wing, she wants to carve me some, so I can be humane, my knife is half-hearted, if kill wasps I must. I can't see what all the fuss is about, so much steam over practically all one does. Olive wasn't brought up to feel inferior, she would have been cross with her mother if she had, she wonders what it's like to be a blackbird, when a pair is searching for food, what's uppermost is to be a blackbird not a robin and look for blackbird-food, the hen doesn't quake and mutter through clenched beak, I am a second-class blackbird. But, it occurred to her, when the mallard fly in, the drake breasts the wind, does the duck feel mortified? If she'd been brought up to see that the world and his wife feel she's inferior, a sense of belonging might have followed, instead, she gets punished, for arrogance she's not conscious of. I'm not surprised! I don't know which is worse, to be in the hands of someone who loves one, or of someone who does not. It seems women are wet, but that when women are tough it's no good either, women should point the finger a little more at themselves. How to be rid of her! Oh, I'm determined we shall be. Under every gruff, seeping exterior may be a person who doesn't have the knack and provokes the wrong response, hen humans are farther from being animals and so for her trickier, she's become nervous and pursues ill-judged conversation, all one can do when like a woman one has no presence of mind is wait for the misery to fade. I do wish she wasn't so triumphant in the garden, triumphant and unstoppable, yet I have only to say the word. Locked in the fruit cage, she wondered which Amazon was the first to cut off a breast, the swifter to throw a spear or draw a bow, and which last, which Amazon had the gumption to make shield and weapon to accommodate breasts, from Amazons she progressed to girl grooms, why don't girl grooms imagine their brains have run to seed and bear grudges against men because of it, is a horse so much less deflating to live with than a man, are mares and foals, why, if one has nature's clothes to wash and nature's bottom to wipe, even with a machine, does one's brain have to go lazy, is straw so different from socks? Olive is unsuitable, it isn't what I envisaged. At her ease among the currants, she thought, uncouth, the currants are glad to become a pudding, she begs them not to be too delicious in that pudding, dissemble, she says, dissemble, she is low in the pecking order, lest her pudding be remarked on by our visitors, let me be, she tells the currants, stupid, or, rather, let me mind my being stupid, I am often stupid but I don't care enough, may my cocksureness be taken away, let me have a low opinion of myself, and be squashed, as you will be, made into a pudding, and gulped down thoughtlessly. She staggers to her feet, stiff, women are frightful, and she is frightful because she is a woman, she tries very hard not to be frightful, the harder she tries the more frightful we, women, find her, she takes up her fruit, pokes her finger through the wire, breathes whiffs of rust and galvanised wire into her nostrils, doesn't feel better, women don't feel better, they brood and don't, waggles her finger until she shoots the bolt. Olive thinks she isn't fit to live with women, with their, our, it seems, inflamed hearing! I attribute the crassest things to her, she says. I understand her better than she thinks, if not crass her ideas are gratuitous.

Hidden Bandages

was not quick enough, he walked straight through Hölderlin, and I winced, so he asked me what the matter was. You'll have to pile into the back, I said to Hölderlin, otherwise he won't understand and will think me standoffish. Why isn't there room for your legs? If you shift that can there will be. I expect it's a petrol can. Is it a petrol can? Oh, it's an empty petrol can, I told Hölderlin. There's a law against carrying petrol. You can carry petrol, but not in a plastic can. You have to carry it in a metal can. Hölderlin said he didn't want to carry petrol, I said sternly, he wasn't. How curious, Hölderlin said, their traffic lights are quite the opposite of ours, red we go, green we must stop, who goes, they go, no, they do, they go on red, at home we stop, green is go.

It makes a fool of me, our driver remarked, one might suppose that the things there are to hear would be cancelled out, that the sense would atrophy. Hölderlin won't relax, he peers between our shoulders, picking at the wicker of the picnic basket which was dumped in his lap. Yet the world is full of little birds, our old friend continues, opening their mouths and throats, the breasts and throats swell, not a note reaches my ear, but my eye catches more notes and their swellings than my ear would have heard songs, more beaks and their yawning. Hölderlin brushed a tear from his cheek, his compassion is easily aroused.

I believe, said Hölderlin, that was a living creature we squashed, shoosh, I said, our friend didn't realise and it's unkind to draw it to his attention, it was very small and made no bump, I suspect he notices only when he feels the wheels go over a bump. That's logical.

The tooting of horns passes him blissfully by, too bad if they're in a hurry, police sirens, and, somebody might be bleeding, said Hölderlin, but inside, I replied, trained personnel are staunching it, was it so unearthly, as it seemed, or peaceful, do you, I wrote, suffer from tintinnabulation, he squinted, oh, not for years now! I'm oblivious to larks, but hawks I've always spotted, he pointed up through the windscreen, hold on, said Hölderlin, to a kestrel on a telegraph pole, you don't have to be so nervous, I said. It's a kestrel, he told me. That was a kestrel, I told Hölderlin, who said mildly, I know!

I think the car acts for him as a kind of willing mule, he kicks it, gaily it responds, he makes good speed, almost too good, it is a bit hair-raising. I hear more and more the splintering of wicker. Is there a hammer under the bonnet, asks Hölderlin. The hawks and miles of dual carriageway are left behind and it's becoming England. Cheer up! I said. But as we were studying the consequences of a new by-pass a person approached us, our friend wound down his window with a genial smile, it was futile, I couldn't answer such questions and we had to abandon her, she was puzzled, said Hölderlin, oughtn't you to mention the frightful clatter, we'd quenched our thirst on our coffee and he was upset, a hand had fumbled for the thermos in his groin. Don't worry, she'll be laughing as soon as we're out of sight, *he* says, they think I'm quite funny and you're a foreigner. Hölderlin listened to that, which was meant as reassurance, with an aura of panic.

I shan't come in with you, young lady, he says, I have someone I'm rather looking forward to seeing. You're extremely welcome. I was touched. I'll fetch you in due course. You've brought a glorious day with you. It's so rural! I said, put the basket beside the rug, and climb out. Quick! Hölderlin trails after me, his face showing foolish relief. Nobody is surprised. In fact, what a glorious day you've brought with you, they say.

Uneventful too, it proved, didn't it? Only a slight embarrassment when the host caught a glimpse of a buttered scone as it disappeared into my pocket, the wicker may have been molested, I was sure its contents hadn't.

I've come for you, he says, did you have a nice time, and, rather shyly, shall we take a turn around the garden, he is looking at me and Hölderlin, the others are silent, perhaps wary.

I was terribly fond of it, I can't forget where I stuck my hands, are we out of earshot, I can't forget, although I want to. I used not to be able to imagine how in the spring it would change, or in summer the stillness of winter, now I see it all, all at once, it blossoms and dies back, waxes and wanes, under my eye, is that second childhood, or dotage. Dotage, says Hölderlin, shut up, I say. How do you manage your city life? I can't manage mine, and it gets worse. It's lumpy, he cries, so lumpy. I wonder if I should have collected you at the gate. The shadows, have you thought how rare shadows are becoming, a threatened species, mm? Shadows aren't shade, masses and masses of that, shadows have character and form, how does one step on shadows that are intensely familiar and not feel queer? Hölderlin shivers. The hedges are leggy! Look at the lawn, my velvet lawn! They should set traps for the moles, they don't understand, a soft heart doesn't really answer. I suppose they haven't the skill, oh well, they haven't. You must wear gloves! I'm not the fellow to pop off through a window. You keep a pair of gloves for mole, he smells you on the metal. It's been allowed to burgeon, and run away, it disgusts me to see the roses not dead-headed, sopping paths, all overgrown, I'd like to take my trusty blade to it, that I would! Funny how frustration can make one wildly unhappy, and I'm not entitled to feel frustrated. It's a meadow! The mowings aren't swept up. The leaves weren't, in the autumn. They belong in the compost heap. Take trouble with a compost heap and it'll reward you. I begin to be aware of an ominously glum figure.

It is disordered, the figure says, it's lovely, I think it's a lovely garden, crammed with oddities. The arms are whirling in our van, trenches to hinder the couch, the arms say, stop the horsetail from casting its spore into the wind, foresight, the arms say, for heaven's sake, foresight! And what's that??! I write, it's being cared for until it gets well. Gets well? It's badly hurt. It's done for, and it knows it, the eyes are filmed over, its eyes are dead already, one wants a bit of resolve, far better bump it on the head, he says angrily. But I can't interfere. Oh, why did I imagine I'd forget, where each tree and plant . . . He grins. I whisper to Hölderlin, whose chin is digging into my shoulder, our friend is working himself up to a sorry state. Those are monsters, says the latter, monsters, it's to no purpose, to stamp on them, they rear up and seed after a complete mangling! I met a rabbit here, just here, that had lost its wits in the snow, lying snow takes on a dull, sullen look in England, does it with you too, like the eye of that poor bird, of any animal, dying resentfully. Ho! my old syringa. But I should have cut off that twisted limb, it's hanging on a thread, why? Why? It's untidy, isn't it. The ideal instrument for monsters is a hook, for all the gross weeds. I miss weeding. The warm soil at the beginning of summer, the clammy at the end. Perhaps I liked my weeds better than my flowers. When the big ones rise to taunt one it's the moment to whet a blade, or they're all of them up to one's neck, and dragging at one's legs. If there are orchids they should be visible, otherwise they're wasted, well, if no one can see them they are. It isn't as though one wants to sense the untrammelled power of . . . whatever it is. Hölderlin whispers, nature? *He* laughs miserably. I suppose it's a beloved adversary? In that bramble bush a wren nests. I ought to have destroyed it. You chop it all down, burn it, and then go for the roots, you have to grope for them, it's akin to delivering a baby, drawing out a bramble root. I've never delivered a baby. I've delivered bramble roots. They are buggers. Oh mind out, fierce wasps feed on the willow sap. See? Bent double and urgent! Hölderlin nods sagely.

Well well! Have you thought, dear, the most precious of all memories are smells, the garden has a sweet reek at night, in the summer, this garden in particular. If I could cart if off with me! One is so trusting, isn't one. I *trust* it, a smell, to be from time to time in my nostrils again. They're unsummonable, smells. I'm astonished that it's possible. To smell a smell which isn't there. Do you smell smells which aren't there? It does astonish me.

I dream often, too often, I've done some very bungled grafting, that I've done it in winter, in an icy wind, I've had to, been forced to do it early, with puddled clay, one can, you know, graft with clay, it lacks the finer points of wax, and makes the job altogether more difficult, yes, am tormented by those absurd, tiny limbs, amputated and bandaged, on other amputations, the sap isn't rising, absurd grey bundles, their bandages hidden, the clay will dry and pale, or in heavy rain melt, the grafts drop away anyhow, because they've failed. Hölderlin whispers, even in a garden, wounds beyond repair.

It pings, mine does, jumps and bangs, so I do have an inkling, of how it may have felt, sometimes it hurts, the hurt sits on my breastbone, the hurt is an acrobat, and I can't breathe, although air goes in and out in an orderly fashion, and my wind is still top-hole, we two old things, didn't we toddle out for our constitutional, for a fortnight together, each time it leaves me it's as if, the hurt, I have no memory at all of it, saliva doesn't yet hang in thick threads from my lips, when I'm digesting my dinner, I don't have to stand tears and dirt and their being wiped from the furrows of my cheeks, I have a rheumy eye, both will soon be rheumy, more rheumy than his, I wonder what rheumy eyes betoken, I haven't been intimately acquainted with a boxer dog before, you're awfully oddly constructed, inconvenient, really, for you, with his undershot jaw and teeth that seem to grow in different places, as if for two mouths, his mouth as kind to the hand as a spaniel's, almost soppy of you to be so gentle, when the threads from his lips become runny and drip he has to swallow tummy medicine from a plastic sac with a bottle drawn on it, funny how he doesn't stare at my broken speech, we fought you fellows, inside I shall never forget, have no desire to, long peace, am in the enemy country, can't forget that, if I fall into the wrong language he knows the words aren't his, he speculates, his eyes brighten, we have discussions, he will argue, if he wants to lift his leg umpteen times in Chausseestraße and not in Friedenstraße, but the question, when will they come home, he doesn't address to me, at dusk, at the beginning, he asks, just once, for the garden door to be opened and he gazes towards the garage, then backs in,

thoughtful, for our morning walks we go to the Grieb-
nitzsee, the breeze is fresh and cold there, he springs into
the air, we feel summer in our bones, I am sad he has
always to stay on the lead, he in his prime revelled in his
strength, he doesn't lack for spunk, I too am apprehensive
when confronted by alsatians, he's old, perhaps I too take
it out on little dogs, now there's a thought, it makes me
sad and because he isn't mine and strife can occur and
problems we stick to safety, his friends hail us in the
street and tell him he's out not with his mummy or his
daddy, tomfoolery, as if he didn't know, not with his
parents, and they tell him how tired he is, how he's aged,
he does seem weary as we near the house, but he's been
leaping into the cool, fresh air after my end of his lead, or
foraging for sticks, his ears don't droop of course, they
can't, I have an open mind, they may be healthier, let no
cankers flourish, I see the driving rain drive straight in
and all he can do is hold his head askew and still without
avail and I feel I don't believe in cropped ears, no sooner
in the garden than he wants a game, he hunts for his
gummischuh, the krokodil lurks, so he says, under a
rhododendron where he can't reach it, he drops a
stöckchen at my feet, we sit on the terrace and survey the
new-raked lawn after the winter, the spring and autumn
dangerous, according to the Huns, times for upping and
dying, he is allowed after dark on the sofa, with a special
cloth, he asks, is it yet, it is not yet, I am whacked on the
sofa myself, he sighs, dogs and horses sigh, in the
mountains, Oskar, a church with no boxers but hounds,
and a cow, a bad-tempered ram, two cats, and worms, fat
coils of worms, those people with oval faces in the
twelfth century were certainly accompanied by dogs and
horses, and when I move, for his benefit, to the chair, we
listen to G. Gould, he stares when I eat my supper from
my knees, he thinks I should sit up at the table, I can't
believe that Bach, dog, wanted it played so, or could have

imagined it so, to us it's beautiful, a revelation, I wonder why, and I used even to be irritated, we walk in the afternoons beyond Königstraße where everyone has to be kept on the lead in the forest and our hearts can beat more quietly, I have an ache to see the Havel, I'd like to stand on the shore, but reams of dogs do that, the day is devoted to him, his food is odd, the brötchen, and in my country dogs don't eat macaroni, at half past eleven comes his dinner, at half past ten he's hopeful, I won't be tyrannised, water falls out of the folds in his lips all over the floor, under his brows he glances at me, more, fresh, and more, free of dribble, by two he's contemplating his walk at three, he has cooked heart for dinner.

I must have dreamt and not remembered my dream, I have a pain to see Pfaueninsel, and I don't much like Pfaueninsel, if only from the shore, am not fond of peafowl, never had relations with them, and strict paths, bolt from beauty spots, though as they go Pfaueninsel a pretty nice specimen, no hordes exactly, beauty spots we call them, why not beauty pimples, people are pus, oughtn't to have this beastliness but don't people flock to beauty pimples and lie cheek by jowl in meadows set aside for that and their litter, if they're suffering they hide it well, if no people Pfaueninsel a little paradise, if one a Prussian king, with so many curious trees, and one doesn't object to the architecture, and he had flowers, trouble with flowers at pimples is one can't see flowers for pus, I suppose, Oskar, kings, kaisers and I, I'm an awful kind of petty kaiser, have to die out, we want large privacies, all to ourselves, happy to talk to a dog, when we are conscience-pricked and allow our privacy to become a pimple we at once desert it, we have to die out, perhaps I like dogs for the cloak they give one of invisibility, I have the advantage there, over a Prussian king, such a deep desire to be alone must be wrong, I've a horrible feeling, dog, I've had a dream of heaven and mistaken Pfaueninsel for it, paradise is chock-full of people, it stands to reason, all laughing, too loud, or making sizzling noises, they carry wee walking tape machinery in their pockets and plug in their ears, hoi polloi in paradise frightful, heaven, old dog, is a beauty pimple, and still we don't reach the Havel, we've been to the post office and negotiated enemies and my tail is up, our idyll is quite broken, we are ambushed on an ordinary toddle near the house, I don't cross the road soon enough, don't follow my instructions, don't let him defend himself, daren't, thought it a bitch, loose, whilst we are on the lead, alsatian, he is blameless, too slow on the uptake, I am, have to tug him into the middle, it leaves the pavement, darts after us, horrified windscreens, I see the lips drawn back, the teeth, coward, split second, at his rump, upset and ashamed we limp home, his skin isn't broached, it's scraped, I go silly with salt water, doesn't turn septic, twenty-four hours putrid yellow, am not fit to take care of anything, any creature, clumsy and my brain slips cogs too often, he is kinder to me than ever, I mind his humiliation, I do mind that, it's Easter and we're out of our beds at the crack, we walk to the Havel, he is so gratified, the forest to ourselves, boar not visible, only deer, we feast our eyes on the water from the knoll above Moorlake, cock an ear to the wind, make a run for it, I shan't see Pfaueninsel, not on this visit, and he thinks, today, today, he gazes towards the garage for a long while, he hasn't since the start, I try to explain, a few days yet, to hang on, his wise face, he stays now very close to me, it's palpable, he climbs the stairs when I do, he doesn't lie on his bed there, he props himself against my leg, he goes downstairs when I do, he presses against me, I've found his brushes, he doesn't sigh, he doesn't complain, if I'm flat on the sofa his hindquarters perch on it too, I know he wants them to come, it is long enough, he isn't unhappy, but he is waiting, he brings me on our

last afternoon to a bench in the woods where I can rest
and lies in its shade, that, I reckon, is clever of you, it's
sweltering, I find myself sitting utterly quiet sometimes
and remember the far-away expression in his face when
he must have been feeling it, his dickey heart, and no one
knew about it, he's a bit reluctant to get up, he dawdles
along the ride, and in Friedenstraße, buck up, I say, I have
tasks to do, he stares at me, I assume he lies by that bench
whenever he sees it, we hadn't met it before, he bounces
into the garden, I think no more of it, then he is on the
sofa, I am in the chair, they come, he has waited for them,
three days later he collapses, four weeks and he is dead,
he was careful not to be taken too far from home, he had a
sense he mustn't, his mistress writes, collapse where the
wild beasts could come to eat him up. In the winter
Pfaueninsel only a step across the ice. I too am afraid and
know I mustn't sink down where the wild beasts will
come to guzzle me, I'll try not to grumble if they do. You
so seriously serene, and I with this feeling of sadness.

A Field Day

Into the conservatory I wheel him, and them, his visitors,
and I bring tea things, I pour out tea, I hand them cakes,
tomato sandwiches, ginger nuts, we lean back in deckchairs beneath the ruin of his whatsit, it irritates him
that I call it conservatory, I don't know why, he is
slumped in his pram, his eyes follow it all, he can't speak,
or doesn't try in company, I talk in front of him, I do, he is
quite helpless, that irritates me, and must hear, and
understand, and feel lost, there is a better self in me
somewhere, in the shade, boiling hot, the woman visitor
looks with despair at the broken panes, she might like to
crawl out through them, the paint has gone, the putty
has gone, the whole conservatory has slipped, I say, their
eyes obedient take in binder-twine and flex rigged to
hooks, it's stricken, at any moment an avalanche of glass,
the man puts a soothing smirk on his face, the vine,
with wizened grapes, loops over our heads, his cheek in
his pram is gently patted by jasmine and plumbago,
orange and lemon trees are blackened by a filthy spider
or some mite, I wheel him into the conservatory, I hear
myself saying, because he is so fond of it, I see the woman
visitor is thinking, his hands, her eyes wander to his
hands, must ache to wipe the leaves, she notices his
hands are puffed and pale, of their filthy black, I expect
the mealy bug, I say, is having a field day, they don't even
smile, the jasmine is strangling the beautiful plumbago,
we're riddled in crook and joint, his woman visitor gropes
for a mealy bug, in a tendril's arm, the white stuff is
pierced by her red nail and red like blood springs onto her
finger, she recoils, that has startled her, fool, I catch tears
in his eyes, redder than the tomato in the sandwiches,

her skin is dyed, she goops from her deckchair up at the withered grapes, sweat stands on his forehead, he glares at me, I smile inanely, and when he has no visitors I carry tea into the conservatory, the pots and crocks have almost to a man tipped over, slats are to blame, the plants that were in them are either done for or bend to the sky, in distorted positions, people at an accident before their legs are splinted, if you want to amuse him, I remark, and life is certainly dull for him, you run out into the garden and scoop greenfly from the lupins, you have to be clever, if they see you coming they all fall off, and feed the goldfish, the woman peers into the tank, no one, she is thinking, is interested in pumping up water often, someone must water or it would be more dead, through the murk you don't see goldfish, they are shy, I say, they sink when they hear voices, the greenfly are immense this summer, their faces are aghast, I have to babble on, the super-greenfly has arrived, the garden is a haven for them, we are surrounded by farmers, all the blights descend on us, the child visitor rubs an orange or a lemon leaf and smears black over its fat slice of cake, it wants to be shown the white haunts of mealy bug and smear red, I am all for the child visitor, well done it, she makes good cakes, its mother is thinking, he doesn't eat, I wonder if he's spoon-fed later, aha, that's what you're thinking, I pour his tea into the invalid's drinking-cup, isn't it a pretty one, so old, the spout bitten in fury by generations of invalid, been in his family, the china is pitted by their teeth, I have slopped in too much milk, perhaps they all had strokes, I have to milk him of urine, I hear myself suddenly saying, and do unmentionable things with his bottom, her crucified existence, they are thinking, tears in his eyes again, in theirs, shock, my mouth drops open and I gasp, the grapes, they think, must have died from embarrassment, another sandwich, I rattle on, it's lovely for him to have visitors, they've dwindled of late, it's a shame, so nice of you to have come, half of him went first, I'm supposed to stimulate the brain, read aloud and teach him the alphabet, you make up for my lack of diligence, he keeps me busy, other respects, you look stifled for air, I fetch hot water and give the door a good flap, I remember, the woman is murmuring, you wrote me a letter once all about wrens, didn't a pair move into the greenhouse during a spell of severe weather, perhaps I've been stung by an insect, I feel I'm half paralysed, I hear myself utter such horrid things, I have to utter them, I must speak, I must, it's a form of crying, don't birds panic, intelligent wrens, blah blah, flew in and out, chink of light wouldn't shut, lived greenhouse five weeks, blah blah, perfect sangfroid, left as they'd come. His visitors try to talk to him naturally, these tell him their news, they talk to him of his affairs, I interrupt, I break their threads, it's uphill work for them. He had a duck, I say, if its ornithology they want to discuss, I thought her charming, he ugly, she sauntered in while he was at his tasks, he said she couldn't do any harm because she had no appetite for tomato plants, it was her habit to, he let her, she made a mess, a dreadful mess, I see bewilderment in the visitors' eyes, total comprehension in his, he would walk through it and walk it into the house, she bathed in the precious dew puddle and it stank, after his second go I said she had to, I was resolute, a duck and a wheelchair are too much together, they were a fine pair, he couldn't speak, she couldn't speak, too late to retrieve that, press on, she liked to plod into the conservatory for her afternoon nap, in the dust, to settle onto her breast beside him, they dozed, the two of them, I suspected her of harbouring mites, sulphur, the man says, sulphur for the greenhouse, her muck clung to the tyres, I'd have to struggle with him all around the lawn, I hosed it off until I hosed him and had to change all his clothes, all, then his rug dragged in it, well, what is a duck, they look strained and wriggle, the cacti sit smugly above their sleek hair, it was an unnatural life for her, she must have been lonely, always been wild, half tame, and timid, nets came to nothing, it took me weeks, weeks and weeks, I caught her with a tit-bit, it was sheer trust that did it, when at last I held her she was light, just feather and down, beak and bone, very touching, I packed her into a cardboard box, she had to dirty that, and into the boot, she could fly a bit still, at two in the morning one might find her, white through the dark, on the roof, she was young, when I was her friend I called her often out of a tree, no mean feat, she was so shy that if she heard the undertaker and his dalmatian in the lane she froze, she could utter faint nasal whimpers of distress, she clenched her beak and vibrated her tongue, I drove her to a mere, a nice, homely mere, as it happened I didn't spot her sort of duck, but birds have instincts and must use them, I opened the lid, she squatted in her muck and didn't move, I poked her, she sprang straight into the air, I'd pictured myself waving a hankie to her as she swam to little and more suitable companions, she flew, the oncoming circle of swans and ducks, they expected buns, pulled up short, I saw her peering down, they seemed appalled, so comic, her crop was empty, an aid to weak wings, she flew and flew until she was lost to sight. I'm sure she found her feet. The woman visitor says rigidly, isn't freedom ambiguous, if one isn't equipped to use it, fed all her life, half tame, isn't freedom, blah, it was only on sufferance her home, I hear myself saying, the tears *well* in his eyes, toiling for an invalid is not fulfilling, it makes one unhappy, and she smelt, the man steals a glance in his direction, the plumbago, I want to change our drift, still contrives to make us shaky blue flowers.

THE GREAT WHITE WORM

from the deaf man's conversation book

Owê war sint verswunden   alliu mîniu jâr!
ist mir mîn leben getroumet,   oder ist ez wâr?

(O woe, these years of mine, where have they all
gone! Did I dream my life, or is it true?)

Walther von der Vogelweide
c. 1170–c. 1230

You'll have to speak up. Oh don't bellow. I'm no more thn a LITTLE hard of it.

CAN YOU READ THAT? Nothing amiss with yr eyes then!

I believe the brain cells feed on sugar, like bees, with not enough to eat they pop off, mine are poppg off all the time, I spoon-fd thm but one cn take a horse to watr, why they won't opn their mths I don't know, have you any idea? I give thm treats, to whet thr appetites. Ppprmint crms!!! You've hit on the rt thg, they may pick up yet.

I'm very fond of brackn, am devoted to it, you cld bring me a bunch. I miss the scent. Grn brackn. to bury my nose in. In the old days, one used to spk of a nose house, do you remembr, I can't alwys turn my thghts in cheerful directns, the roof lay on one's nose, and the nose pointd up to hvn. We bed-riddn lack brackn, it doesn't occur to any 1 to brng it, they lug sweet flowrs, hyacinths, & those yellw whatsits, brown plastc bulbs, I like sour flowrs, they think I'm gaga if I ask 4 sour flowrs. Are you going it? Gaga.

Well I'm pinnd down in bed. Chilld to the marrow oftn. Unnatural cld it does take itself off but one feels it nevr will. Are you the 1 who brght me ppprmints? Our insides go rottn, bad, that's why we keep the windows shut, you cn opn thm if you're stifled, but you'll let the flies in, they are attractd, a bird comes to eat the flies, is shy howevr & whilst you sit there won't. The opium poppies decay on their feet, our bodies like to do it in bed, so 1 has the worst of both worlds.

You think a grasshoppr will jump at last min. from under yr foot & it doesn't, you are still compos mentis &

the grasshoppr which you expectd to live is compost on the path.

1 thinks, tomorrow, gone, but 1 isn't!

Or we cld play chess, you might have to rmd me, my mmry not foolproof.

I drm! every knight.   of dogs, puppies. Of doing sthing wrong with thm, I carry armfls of pups swhere & I have WORRY over thm. I have to carry armfls back, I wake before I cn, I'm not so clevr cn you explain tht, it wld be nice to have an inklg bec. I drm it too reg. for comfort, we've nevr had dgs. 0 to do with thm. Pups. I'd be happ. to drm of cats. And 3 nights ex 5 I have thm myself! Or I guess thats how they must be born, they have no othr mothr you see, it embarrsss me, in the drm. Your not squeamish are you

Is it a war wd. Vast nos. got those, or were gassd, you're nevr up to much once you've bn gassd.

Haven't bn rained on since 1979 dear.

I'd ask for some 1 who loves and understands me to go thro' my thgs, that's all its not so

But seemgly imposs.

Neithr loves nor understnds. Only GOOD! & goodness isn't enough. It's funny. If you care to cm more we shld get acquaintd. I have a feelg it has to be a womn tho'.

Are we?? I forget. Are they flourishg?

In my drawrs may be thgs not fit, will you? the 2nd frm bottm, wld you mind? it's ages. If I keep on peekg nothg will arrive in it not fit. I fear I concentrate on my correspondnce.

I read as vociferously as ever, & I am still quite dextrous. Oh it nevr lets up proprly, I take a lot of pills & they give me disgustg drms you know, they're a kind of cheese. I watch the TV & radio. I don't like tht Wmn, do you? I don't like him eithr. The othr 1.   the 1 in America. Its sickng I find. 1 or t'othr, 8 x a day.

1 doesn't want to go without leavg the country in safe

hds. You have no objectn to dying, have you? Did you brng the drwr. I look forwrd to being hauld out of bed, that'll be refreshg. She has sold all our assets & squandrd the proceeds a child cld tell her that is !!false econ. I AM perturbd. Also I don't fancy hangg rd tht Wmn as a ghost, it wldn't be at all pleasnt, so I try to dampn my interest in politcs, I'm not jokg it wld be frghtfl, you cn become a gh. inadverttly, I have no desire to see what she eats for breakfst. Unless I cld ration what she fds her brn-cells, wld tht be disastrs or bettr do you

Have you bn watching TV too?!!!!

They are loosg polar bears in Som. Bec. the mink are ovr-plentifl, & polar bears are ideal for wipg out mink. They are a bare mthfl for thm. There are kangs. in Yorks. You spot thm in yr hd-lts as you drive home across the mr. Must add spice to the journey. It was! In the Alps, your attachd to the Alps you shld learn what you mght meet they've releasd an anim. from the Him.s. Not llamas, thats Andes, what else is there, reel off some names. They are jumblg the wld on purpose, so as to educate us, there have bn reindeer on Cairngorm for umpteen   No! YAK.

She shld spend more hrs by her TV, with a weathr eye on the TV you don't lose touch, she's bn sellg off miners by the score

You're a man so you're clevr, you cn tell me, I think there must be

                    use the strainer

an element of trth in evrythg, how else cld it be, there has to be an elt of trth, even when we die, it's only lgcl? But 0 body sees what I mean. In drms & thghts, all the untouchable, some germ, we have no othr source, when you & I are gaga we shll retain an elt of truth in our noddies, do we take it with us

I donT have any inclinatn to arrive in whats foreign I shld be lost I think there has to be an elt of trth, it can't be shakn off? cn you tell   It wld relieve me of a WORRY

A wmn's logc is perilous, that's why 1 ought to be perturbd. I had to stop knittg. You have to put up with a glimpse, they chnge the picture at top speed, so quickly you cn be confusd, perhaps if she watches it she gets confusd thats why she doesn't. I glance at it from time to time I catch more thn if I stare, that's the way with glimpses, you mustn't look into thr eyes

Once we had elt in our forests, do you remembr, they're long gone, the noble elt
— great timid creatures
the snow stoppd, they missed the snow, she doesn't approve when I spill so I don't drink it any more, they have bearded chins, lickd the flakes, I am too cold, they weren't cold enough, & are obsolete

it cld be, we grow coldr, & coldr, until too cold, & then V. tired.

Pl do cm agn to see the old crock!! Was sweet of you to brng me the yellw thingummy

The Big End

It's making a noise.

Will you STOP.

It was making a funny noise. I don't know, I can't judge how terrible.

It was a knock.

The power seemed to be failing. Didn't you sense that?

At my shins.

The steering?

Describe to me what that is.

If I've got the idea I don't think cars have them any more. Oh, why must they?

And where is the crankshaft?

Really?

Under foot was

If you're going to lie down, do do it on the rug. I was considering your clothes, not you! Have you some rags? Don't you carry clean rags with you? Well, it doesn't seem typical of you, that's all. Surely the windscreen won't object that once in a while you borrow its?

Seized up?

I can't drive.

Because I never learned. I'll lie down instead. I trust you not to run over me. Is pushing not the same? Only a few inches then. I look where? You believe it will bend? It's solid metal! How could it? Actually? Don't we see already if it's soft? I haven't experienced such fatigue.

It doesn't. It stays straight, and revolves.

How many miles?

Are those the mountings? Is the engine fast.

That you should NOT! It's far for a noise to go. You'll do it injury. Your car. By pressing it.

You are doing injury.

Loud.

I! You remain. There may be coffee in the thermos. A telephone box? Do STOP. Perhaps a passing driver will

Why not?

If I don't you'll know that is what has happened to me.

Weren't you joking?

At the next farm! It's still warm. Tell me, what do I say? Have you a membership number?

On, or back?

The mechanic is coming.

They were milking. So sweet. Should I have offered to pay for it? Is it dear?

It could be a breakdown van. A mechanic in any event.

Oh!

Do you expect an angel to do the gardening? No human will perform the precise tasks you would yourself undertake. Does it affect the crop? Does it matter if some apples are smaller? Is dead wood bad? Some people have nausea. Do you water young trees through the summer! For how many summers. The water in the ground must be quite high. Not everyone approves of that. It may not be so new-fangled. They taste better without. They do! Was it hard? Hard going? I ate too many strawberries. Do you fork the herbaceous border each autumn without fail? Do they have to be divided, why? Had a lot got lost? Very lost? Were you upset? Very? I am sorry!

A white owl, and not yet dusk. I want to walk away a couple of paces.

She's having a decko, does that mean a look?

Dekko?

She says, she may have to tow you in. She thinks the head gasket, it has gone. Is that serious?

It bubbles.

Under your own steam would be possible. It doesn't cost any more if she hitches you up.

She says I was wise.

She says, you're not to grumble at me! You might have noticed you were <u>hot</u>.

I'm fine.

Ah in the old days, she says, it was a different matter, those lovely motors, then one had to DD clutch, what on earth? it isn't that I'm too young, it's a problem with the words.

I haven't broken down with anyone before, and it's not in any of the lessons you ever have.

Speaking of which, she says,

Lovely motors probably!

They bought a dog, not with an eye to show, but they wanted a good one. A setter.

English S.

They had the pick of the litter, she says. The dog hasn't turned out as hoped.

Faults.

The temperament is perfect, with children, in society, ours and theirs.

How, whose?

Canine.

He goes too close behind. He doesn't carry his tail gaily, he's either over-abashed or over-cocky.

Poor beast.

And his head isn't. Wait please. He lacks <u>nobility</u> in the head, the dome is too shallow. That's the worst.

They don't love him less, they love him without pride. Their eyes light on him with disappointment. Could you open the bonnet once more. She says, should they be saddened by the dog because he's not a beauty or should the dog be disappointed in them. No tow-rope, we'll be lifted into the air by the forewheels. That's how it works. Are you out of gear? Particular kinds of person desire a dog to be a good-looker, she says, why? No one minds a horse that isn't, to horses we're indulgent.

You don't stay in it, we're to travel in the cab with her.

The sire and the grand-dam were champions.

The children play in the garage.

They dare not teach them an animal can be dispensed with, even to another nice home. Besides! They don't want to. Our thermos, you were sitting by the hayrick.

She didn't hear you.

He's a character.

You remember wheels that wobbled, broken springs and half shafts? Weren't lamps so dim in thick fog a passenger had to walk waving a torch? True adventures. Big ends!

They were the noises.

And two of his teeth are undershot, although as a pup he had a perfect mouth. One can't see teeth. You simply know they're wrong. Then you feel very guilty!

She said, those are her real clothes, if she has to tog herself up she loses no time climbing back into them. And that people are lucky to have real clothes, if they do have them, that if they have them they should wear them, some, or many, go all their lives without real clothes, in a series of outfits, trying to please.

Drowning the Noise

How strange, all one's life, to listen to the waterfall, when other folk live where no water falls and have less silence. Perhaps we need a drowning agent. We could have a glass of milk and graukäse in the alm, if you like? I sat in the winter garden, on my own, only deadness in my mind, and felt as though I'd had a stroke, I couldn't speak, words refused to come to lips, knew I hadn't, had a stroke, could flex all joints, dreaded encounters, I stared and fumbled for the right greeting, the polite, it was easier to sit quite still in the winter garden, so peaceful, and plant it again and again with orange trees in tubs, flowering pots, creepers, and think of pineapples, I sat at a table, pawing the cloth, the trees were thinning, it rained, and rained, and felt dead. In winter the waterfall is frozen, you know, there's no noise at all, a hush, one wakes surprised. No one hears it his life long, we come in summer, and are impractical. It's all so deceptive, we interpret and mis-interpret, and we misinterpret so much of what happens, what's said to us. On so still a day sounds fall aside, as we rounded the bluff it died abruptly, and the white water in the valley. People may be shy of speaking to you of that. They milk fifteen, and have fifteen heifers higher. They remind me of so many sets of teeth. It must have been torn apart in the ice age, on one hand the teeth, on the other the spines which fitted into the palates. But he should put a post in it and give you a crown, save it! I wonder what they think about, these people, who live on the mountain, with their cats, what does a cat think, transported to the alm, for the summer, near the freshly-falling snow. I no longer know what to think, my brain has burst. I don't understand anything any more, it's no use asking me, I'm sure there should be a remnant that can function, but it seems not, time goes by and it's no better. Chamois? Their horns were straight? Chamois have some white on the face. Antlers? Roe deer? She to the fore! Why so uncamouflaged in summer coats? When a poor worm. In the tepid pools little worm creatures, with snouts and legs, they have the glittery grey and copper as if stuck on, as it appears in the stone to be, under water, it seems to have dimension, unless they move one sees nothing but the usual bed. Dozens of them. Deer run faster than worms. You'd far better take it out, otherwise it'll cause you grief later, breathers are good. The sock too. You take care, I notice, not to hurt a gentian, is it sentiment really? Is sentiment to be disparaged? It's useful, to all those gentians, if not to you. Only sentiment makes me accompany you with stren-uous work besides the walking. I know I look calm, it's a trick I learnt long ago with livestock. It has to be drowned, life, it makes such a clatter. I come where it is all drowned, and I haven't recovered, I am still dead. Nothing's stirring. I can't help it, have you ever had one which you didn't probe with the tongue? One can tell at last the difference between weeds and flowers, flowers grow where weeds cannot, so high! That's luck for us, they hate walking to a spot which leads nowhere, the marking is ancient. It must be pure, no glacier, no hut above us, you can drink. Qualms are unnecessary. I'd have rather plodded on, and quietly slipped my bolt, without any excitement, without the noise and the drowning. One can force oneself, but the result is disgusting. All my ideas have no wings. They are salami. Perhaps dying is like this, caught before one has finished. An egg? It's chilly. You're not chilly? I dread false teeth, yet people cope with them without a murmur, it astounds me, umpteen people cope. They begin to be near. I shall clack and suck when I eat, if I can eat, or talk, and feel mortified. You're spared that then. I know I am, youngish, that's why it strikes me. If false teeth didn't exist, would these precise mountains remind me of teeth at all? Is it my fear, or is it their ability to come out and spend the night in mugs, where they attract the eye more. Better we weren't so clever, someone cudgelled his brain and a pink plate popped out. Nature and art, two old-fashioned aunts, they hang, looming, over one, demanding a hand to shake, and one is doubtful, aunts they may be, are they quite benign, one used to blink at those stiff aunts and wonder why the parents pitied them, I couldn't grasp what with aunts was in the air. But without music, without paint, without words, would nature still resound? Do I have to be intimate with false teeth to admire the mountains, before they became universal who bothered to climb? And our primitive idea of mass and form, have we absorbed it from nature or nature it from us, when we fiddle and arrange it, if that were so, why should we reckon one peak more beautiful than another, it's most unfair to them, why aren't all equally, and how could that fellow remark on the beauty of a mountain he has known all his life, perceive that from the west, on the west flank, it is a beautiful mountain, his cousin meanwhile keeps a few miles down the valley a chamois head on his wall made of plastic, and we, you and I, judge him a dolt, don't we, he may not be any such, he is surrounded, too, by rock that was spat out in the ice age, thoroughly plastic, or whenever that spitting happened, you're more of a geologist than I, or he may already have false teeth, or think artificial chamois decenter than dead. Test it! If we consider our inventions so original we deceive ourselves, we could do with a child to send across. And when each of us becomes his own little artist, with our inventions and imaginings about each other, art is very terrible, we are frantic with them, and call them embellishments, senile we have an excuse, sad how dirty they get, to senility belongs the last fertile moment, have you ever fallen through? Yet it's our function to think, to think until there are no thoughts left and we can expire, so we're in a downright quandary. I did slither once, some lengths. Possibly it's life, not aunts, that hangs over us, full of unkempt emotions, ripe for embellishment. It ought to be ignored. I do! I can't sit in the winter garden, pawing the cloth, I run, I have to crawl off the map almost, these days, to lay my head in the lap of nature, one aunt in the winter garden, and one aunt in the mountains. I may catch sight of it, something, again, just as it's slipping away, like an animal, making itself invisible, or the sun, when I'm utterly weary.

Raining Down Dung

In the blue you know there's a horse-angel, she loves us so much she lives up there to make dung, well she drops it over the earth of course, she makes us fertile, she sleeps in a stable, I think it must be chilly at night, the sun disappears, stars pretty feeble, the moon isn't warm, the dung has to be shovelled out at dawn, any later it would splatter us, why do you look so sad, a boy is sometimes needed, he fills her rack with hay, he scythes grass for her, he's kept busy, he feels his worth, the horse-angel is mighty sweet to him, he is her companion, she's been working harder these days, she is his companion, she has to be everlastingly dung-spreading, more dung is demanded, she is glad he puts his arms around her, the earth is poisoned, she's often weary, gratitude from below is small, his willing arms are needed, the earth is forced, poor earth, to poison boys, more boys are being poisoned, the earth is not to blame, the horse-angel listens to the earth's crying, she listens tenderly, she tries to make more dung, richer dung, she's splitting her sides to make dung, the earth cries, what walks on two feet pays scant attention, or doesn't cop the gist, the horse-angel will forgive you because you have no ears, you aren't unlucky, I'm not unlucky either, don't be distressed, you may remember when you wander out before dawn in your pyjamas and the dung misses your head you're already acquainted with the boy who shovels, without ears you might hear the horse-angel when she whinnies, I'm not certain, I shall learn, if you call we may hear you! A shovel will be there, waiting, but chocolate and raspberry would put some iron into me, thanks very much, they spoon it into ancient folk who have no teeth and reckon

Old Needles

The larches lose the lot, the pines and spruces their old needles, but they have young ones, they only bare a little more branch, we shed our new needles and are left with the old, they sprout helplessly from our bare, worn branches, with old needles one can't do much, faded and stiff they won't breathe for us, they have no juice, and what's a bit sad for them is that they retain a memory of how it was, how it felt, they have to, to cling on, they're sure to be wistful, we take for granted not youth or energy but a brain that can sense and order, and dream without hideousness every night, so we cudgel it, we cudgel our brains and are exhausted, we have now to have the strength to raise our arms and hit our heads, and to hold up beneath our own blows. I thought I'd come to the end of what I could do, slowly I saw there was more, far more, I still couldn't do it, and that was worse. The trouble is, people don't wipe their noses on proper hankies, it isn't just women's peeing, or shit, it's better in June or early July, they do melt in the winter. I wonder they dare go into the mines. I beat my head and a whole party of disorganised and disorderly ideas pop out. Perhaps senility is our normal state, writ large. They, the gaga, go gamely on, trying to separate dream from reality, we try to be good, we know we're supposed to. For them, things gone for ever, things more important than walking. We fly our flags. It's most unlikely, you may have swallowed a few amoebae and hydrae, one doesn't get them from those. I groan, but what on earth is it, concentration? That poor creature, she told me she met a youth group, you know how they stream along regardless, she was greeted by the schoolmaster, and she stood aside for a few, the path was narrow, sheer rock and a drop to water, a girl looked a bit ashamed, and one becomes fed up with standing aside for the young, that they're in such a trance irritates one, that they gaze neither to right nor left, that those at the fore can't speak to or often see those at the rear yet all move as a body, are absorbed in being a body, fed up she found a tiny gap and stepped into it, a boy brushed past and his rucksack strap, or buckle, scraped her arm, she saw red and ran at them, thumped a boy, without a word they fell on her, and then with wordless courtesy pulled her to her feet, she crawled off and sat where it was damp and got a chill. If that's what concentration is, we have no business to have it, let alone hanker after it. But it isn't broken, it needs a new battery, why did you buy it if you don't like them new-fangled. I don't mind your having mine, it's wonderfully peaceful without one, the sun does me quite well. I was alone, people seemed to have brought their handker-chiefs, cotton, in pockets, and if there are people it's a grave, it was alive with marmot, they take their ecstasies from nature too, though I hope they know nothing about missed lives, some animals must do, if not on account of the other thing, a smell of rotting in the air, breeze cool, sun burning hot, little falls of shale, and when the marmot whistle my flag flaps and cracks, when the sentinels sit up, sometimes, it's true, nature fails, or I fail to touch the lap, sentinels on stones, they'd been sunning themselves, plump before hibernating, one has to learn the lap can't always be there, has, itself, other things to attend to, <u>won't</u> any more be there whenever one calls out. Because my flag is still flying, I want to lie down on the turf, so high, near the end of all turf, and go to sleep, looking up through my lids at the sky, and not wake. Out of pleasure, not despair!   I'd seen eagles. Eagles! So long as I can know that nature is more lovely than the dream. I can't be light-hearted, I'm very heavy-hearted, I should be revolted, to be light-hearted. Unless I could do that, want to die, I'd reckon myself ill. I'm nervous of dwindling, old needles. I hope it'll be <u>suddenly</u> over, and one can be left feeling rather surprised.

The Great White Worm

Our dear/honourd Friend! if you walk over Alprechtalm to Hasenthal you will see the BLUE GERNiums, they are prolific there, it is quite a common flow. You reach into different CLIME & soil & now this month almost all the flows are either blue or WHITe, it is striking, you can stroll it, in 4 hours gentlY, the ache in the blaDDER y'day should be homesickness, acidity isn't in the cooking of my WIFE, naturally we are charmed if you wisH to remain little longer, even without the bosom acquaintances, is it poss you can't be awarE that other guests are aLL on occasion disturbd, my wife is anxious, LEST we together drive these away, nobody wants to be rousd in the niGht, why don't you cast a glance at your waTCH, it is a beautiful one you take pleasure in admiRing, you can't admire it unlesS you look at it, that would reWard you, in sleep one hears noiSes that render one awake, with day devotd to stretchING of legs in the moUntains guests get difficultY often in passing again into sleeP, MY WIFe works rather hard, it wld be kind of you, food & drink can be arranGED the even before, the balcony has been constructd with eye to dayliGht hours & so footfaLLs tend to THundeR in each of the rooms thereof, the deckchairs are always unwieldY, I can't myself unfOLd without a tangle firsT, it may be comic, but the moon doesn'T SMile, only the sun, your wash can be managD if you don't confUSe clean with needing to be, my wiFE shed a tear when she saw her PILe for the iron had learnt to know other CLOTHEs, it requires an iota of SENse, we might be more accusTomd to applYing it than you, it is a good commodity, worth culTIVatg, we instill it into our childrn, do you not into yours, the table napkin lies in a

RED pocket, each gueSt has oWN colour, you find it by plate with breakfast, other napkins lie within yOur grasP but you are <u>not supposed</u> to eat with them, guests have cerTain privacy around theiR lips, you are fASTIdious & so may they be, my wifE can't probe in time the pockets, a child does ITs best, what a tHEAtre, absentmindedness we likE to indulge, so don'T take it to heart, it isn't that you're locked away so what is natUral is no longer to you natUral, modest & amiable I think warmLY that you are, no, it appearS to me, my wifE is too busy, that your sad lack hearing leadS you to BELieve you can fly innocent throuGh houses leaving no scathing, it is NOT SO, you will be Glad to know it, we all long to be human, indeed you are TRUSTED SOUL, we shall for years to come consiDer you a trusted soul, truly, truly, the babY is too likeLY to choke, grandfatherly though it is of you to be generous to it, little ones are tough, you shouldn't woRRY, the older ones won't choke & are more suitable, you mustn't reckon you've upSET uS or shouLD HuRRy away, regard yourself POPULAR, I write at length as it is handY but won't steal your communication furtheR. You need at least an ice-axe for the gReat whITe WoRM. You are ILL-eQuippeD!

Deaf Eggs

Dreamt. Of a woman who shouted at me, I expect you collect them, cracked females, she was teaching me to sit down, I ought to know apparently, you tuck fingers so, let hind part drop, press with the old thumbs, it's, she bellowed, a knack, you have to <u>believe</u> yr hands won't get squished, the English deckchairs have forgotten how to have arms, you're standing behind, aren't you, to prevent unnerving crash of back strut, no, you should face it, an arm in each hand, it won't crumple up, it has to open correctly, but if you fail with yr thumbs the arms will bend inside-out and dangle inoperative below, didn't you notice you could have arms, it's far more comfy, the most humble one has them, and ample canvas, it's a symptom of sickness, when the arms are lost or forgotten, there must be something the matter with England, I'm afraid I'm bossy, she shouted. And I thought although dreaming, in dreams I know how to open deckchairs, how is that, when ordinarily I make a hash, and she prodded me, it's tragic, she said, to be fated to be bossy, objections bubble up in the breasts of victims, and capable too!

I was wondering, she yelled, in the matter of stings, why should a bee lose its life, and wasp a not? The bee dies protecting its queen, hive, other bees, and only by accident, by <u>mistake</u>, in a sticky situation, it isn't meant to meet yr neck, her breath touched my cheek, and panic when confronted by yr collar, that's a waste of a bee, and if the hive is bumped into by an inquisitive beast, poor beast, it's catastrophic, all the bees dash out and die, even the queen, tipped over and alone inside, may die, and though behind their paint in the stout apartment houses the bees are safe enough, and the nosy beasts, in the alm in summer they're vulnerable, bees die as a last resort, if a bee dies on its own, protecting no one, venturing out, where it has no business, it's as a <u>punishment for individuality</u>, aren't we bursting with it, once we weren't so full of ourselves, so industrious, recording our emotions and petty ideas, fingering the tensions in our little lives, then we got the knack of it, we do it all the time, we treasure it, we pity those who lack it, we have to die out, it can't continue, everyone will be extremely quiet in a common world again, jelly won't be made in rabbit moulds, or tortoise, it'll be a kind of mercy, to be in the swim, I'm sure it's naughty, and she thrust her mouth towards my ear-drum, naughty to be individual, to <u>want</u> to lay one's head, <u>alone</u>, in nature's lap, and have all those shining moments, at the dentist I agree, she shouted, there is a haven of progress, but why should the bee die and the wasp live, the good bee, what does a wasp do, to deserve it, do you know what a wasp does, is the bee good because it makes honey, or is prettier, we eat honey by accident, and, having made me sit in the deckchair, it seemed she would tip me over in it, the bee makes honey for the hive, its queen, and princesses, we <u>steal</u> the honey, bees have to re-double their efforts to feed us, have to dance more, and fly more, and I was tortured in my dream by the thought, all to accommodate our sweet tooth, and if we supply them with sugar for the winter that's an <u>inferior</u> substance, is the good bee good because it conforms, perhaps, or tries to, when we stop trying to be individual shall we be good, we hand out punishments, in our collars, with our nosy beasts, poor beasts, they have to die from stings, the bees collect punishments endlessly, true the wasp is burnt in its own nest, but why should, vis-à-vis the wasp, the bee, stinging, die? She screeched when I told her. It's hard to find one which is attractive, they're such parasites, false premises, and there she blushed, could we live without them or, in my

dream I rather urgently wanted to wake up, are we the
parasites, we build on them, it must be tricky, with a bee
in yr neck, and no warning, to sit so still, in yr lap you
could watch it, I dreamt once, she boomed, I'd lay my
head in a lap, tip it over and lay it, a simple gesture, I
longed to, but didn't, and of all the erotic couplings and,
she rocked me in my deckchair, uncouplings, and
rollings in hay, of youth, and childhood, of grown-up-
hood, as the hay becomes squished, and the bed waxes
unkind, that one desire is the keenest, the most remembered, and that I didn't, ever, lay my head in that lap
remains neither here nor there, it was instinct, the hay
slowly stiffens, and freezes, isn't in the barn but floating
upwards, upside-down, clenching rough mountain to its
belly, the glacier, I thought, she means the glacier, we eye
it from afar, she yelled, the fun has turned serious and
still I want to laugh, out loud, or sneeze, in my dream I
felt I'd been talking too much to him, and listening to his
addled notions, she nudged me, why have the check hens
died out, do you know, did they lay so many deaf eggs
. . . I woke, I didn't know, why they had, I'd have to ask
him, he would . . . I slept, and dreamt on, I doubt if females
will, she was muttering, not cracked ones, we'll hang
around, to unwind yr deckchairs for you, push you into a
sitting position and . . . a Thing was winking at me, across
a crevice, it winked and winked, when the sun went in
one saw straight through its crystal body, the sun shone
and it winked, huge, in the cheek of a rock, a hammer and
some nimble footwork might have got it, it winked and
winked, I turned my shoulder, it started to shout, it
bellowed, I woke and said, how ridiculous, how perfectly
ridiculous, all that shouting, in a dream.

Oh my dear duck if I'm upset I make a cake, I cook, the cake won't taste as it once did, I shan't bother to eat it, never mind, so many drops of coffee, no, almond, essence, so many tears, woe is enticing I'm afraid.

Before he went?

For a short while he had the idea there was a nest of Nazis in the village, Nazis or Nazi-hunters, I'm not to this day sure which, or when the confusion arose, and that they would be taking us away and putting us to death, I suppose he must have died thinking it, it seems very melancholy, until then he was so lucid it was uncanny, even after the second, his speech was slurred, few recognisable words came out, but one saw he was, like the central heating boiler, firing. One seems to do that. Go and die with some cracked notion.

Look at it this wise, we were lucky, almost 43 years of I'd call it felicity, what would you, perfect felicity is wonderful luck, it was disturbed by so little, we never lost that.

I used to wheel him into the conservatory, if we had visitors I brought tea. I quite miss it, after he died it disengaged itself from the house in a storm and slid into a broken pile, the glass cut all the tender, and a frost, the vine lives on, rather silent and crippled. In the conservatory he mixed his old liquid manure, with the soft water, with rain. There are no onions in it, I don't eat raw onions myself, you needn't worry. It has no stink when liquid.

You take horse droppings, and stick them in a watering can. A small shovelful perhaps? You keep a watering can for the purpose. Stir with a split fork handle, wait a half week, squash any lumps left with end of split fork handle, stir again, with vigour, preferably splashing your trousers, and hey presto. It's far from strong, mind you, and not all that effective, does in a hurry or as an afterthought, a reviver. I tended to spoon in the manufactured kind, artificial, lavish helpings, when his back was turned, he was so pleased if the lettuces responded, or the spinach. He spent hours over his watering can, he was devoted to it.

You perforate the soil, with a dibber, and you pour it in, it must reach the root and not burn the stalk, you have to make safeguards if your grip is shaky, some dykes and sea walls, the holes go in aslant, you top up until each seedling has swallowed a good half pint in its hole, and tuck those in.

If I think of liquid manure I see his face. How long can one do that? How long before I have to think of manure to remember his face, shall I one day see only manure and no face behind the split fork handle? Nothing stirring?

In dreams, with utter clarity, when consciously one can't any more, I know.

Twice I've dreamt of a young elephant, she comes towards me, brimming in her animal fashion with love, she stands her fore feet up against my stomach, from an elephant that's really too much African. I persuade the legs to return to earth. Gently. I find elephants' feet make me want to cry. The washer needs changing. I laid a towel out for you! Twice the elephant has come for me, and I wake with happiness, smiling. I hope it was like that for him, elephants not Nazis. Or Nazi-hunters. Of course it was, most odd. The innocent take on the guilt. I hope he didn't imagine the children were Nazis. But a week's delirium after a happy life, long happy? If I seem callous, isn't one, in self-preservation, if one dwelt on what was in someone's head as he died it would be unbearable. That week is in store for me too, you too, it's the spade, fumbling at one's underneath. Preserved for what I wonder. My hands won't go willingly to work. Not for me on my own. I hot-foot it to buy jampot covers, they wait in the drawer, friends I don't like roam through the fruit, Indigo is sleeker and plump, on my meat, on my fish, I'm quite bad at looking after myself. I'd give anything to bring tea to the conservatory once more.

Go out?

Poor pheasant. They nest in those grass bowers and lose the clutch at a fell swoop.

Isn't there always one silly cow, confronted with strangers in a narrow path she swings round, rolls her eyes, would toss her horns if she had them still, makes a bit of mayhem in the herd. So like us.

See how heavy the dew, in the shade, and it's afternoon! No dew in heaven, I'm sure heaven's lacking.

I think, oh why did he have to leave, leave the snowdrops out and the daffodils and primroses, showing leaf, birds in the trees, and the smell of growing.

You're dripping oil, why is that?

I don't suppose heaven's oily.

Drive carefully. Bye bye.

I didn't say you were one.

But you don't have to trot along to see me perpetually to qualify as such, you can be it all by yourself at home.

Hippocratic has nothing whatsoever to do with hypocrisy.

They don't usually. Have you asked your dentist? And what does he think?

Is your bite all it shld be?

Did you box?

The muscles perhaps. Or you've grown too aware of it.

I once did myself, none of us is immune, produced them, the whole caboozle, not a stray among them. No tell-tale red ⋈.

The correct symptoms, to a man, the nth°.

I had to forget it. Very shaming.

Daresay you haven't. Wide open!

Have a wrench ever?

Might account for it. Teeth done when? No trouble? Does it condescend to go back at night?

How soon after breakfast.

And when loose, stays loose? You might cultivate little naps. No grinding while dozing then. Am astonished. Thought you grinding chap. Plenty of sweet sleep.

Why is it fine now?

It's fine.

How can it know it has to behave the min. it comes to see me.

I shld have run out to intercept you in the st.

I expect you're prey to odd sensations, you know.

It's shut at the moment in the ord. manner.

Always when you're alone?

What do you do then.

Is it painful?

Do people notice? You sound the same? Do teeth ache later? The gums?

Salt and water.

Jolly lucky to be dwelling on that end of you.

Prostate/piles/gangrene! Gout/var. veins, all passing you by?

Not confined to wn.

You'll have to bring it while misbehaving.

Sleep?

Do you SLEEP

Those not my dept.

We can all do with a bit of brutal turning-around sometimes.

Delighted. Hang on. Not finished with you.

Those teeth meet, tongue isn't enlarged, tonsils intact and blooming. It's daft.

If it is, may be a signal.

Talk less.

I'll have a specimen of urine.

Protein.

Can't be bothered to obfuscate.

A sterile one, you do it in the wee jug which you come upon in that sealed envelope, you cover it with the paper towel and carry it thro' the waiting room without stumbling.

Got to keep it, no help if melancholy.

You off foreign parts?

D'you have banging when you go up them?

How fast?

Tap it on table.

Good. And wind?

That's imposs. Nobody breathes more easily in thin air. Well so long as you're not light-MINDED. Watch your steps?

Eh? I never have. Pity. Can't do it all in this whatnot.
You might have learnt to lp-rd.
Blow 2 languages, why not 1 to start with.
I'll listen to it while you're   with your   Ha ha!
Body practices a great deal of deception: what I'd like
to know is why? why?
Often no point. Not cry, not sign distress, not smoke.
Yet not always harmless diversion. Pure arbitrariness.
Dp brths!
Circulation? The old feet?
Roll it up. It's a new machine, high acc., against
mercury level.
Tiptop. Nearly.
I'll have a look. Stare at the rabbit.
Straight at my little light. MY little l. Steady as you
If you're driving I can't dilate them. You may have but
you certainly <u>shouldn't</u>. Not content with being   !
Going to retire early.
Decrepitude.
Am not quite the thing, wish I had your   ha ha!
Tummy trouble. Until January.
You mustn't leave it too long. All the best. Don't forget
to pee for Cynthia.
Cheerio.

Privacy

I thought, you had a car, I did not, it's always fatal to think. You'd said, if we were going to be in the same region it would be nice to meet. I agreed, didn't I agree fervently. It would have been. But then you wanted me to come to the coast. I hadn't seen it meant, I join you. I might have, it wasn't ruled out. If I'd been in Yugoslavia and had found a spot to leave my things in. I wasn't in Slovenia after all. I think you assumed I'd be coming. I doubted. I wanted to see you, very much, but I doubted, over the 'phone, I'd come to the coast, very much. You couldn't hear my doubt, and it evidently wasn't relayed, you don't make allowances, for the diff in communicating with you, it isn't easy, when it has to be relayed. You may not have pictured, did you stop to picture, one doesn't, how I was weighed down, in all fairness you couldn't know I'd set out with too much to carry when I usually travel light. I was exhausted. It's diff with a car, you've absolutely no idea how diff, until you've tried it, one becomes a littler per altogether. You couldn't give me an address, you didn't know where you'd be staying, of course it's small, of course I could have found you, though it's diff with a car, I was apprehensive, how much did it cost, where you stayed, where should we have eaten, perhaps it was too small, where was I to stay, I expect it was boring, such a small place, without me, and swimming, the beach, I've given up swimming, it doesn't matter why, I didn't have unlim money, what I had was to stretch, you unfort came at the beginning, when I couldn't be sure how well it would. I doubted I'd turn up, wasn't free to gallivant all over Europe, wearing enough as it was, I didn't have clothes for the Adriatic, or rather, I had clothes not for the Adriatic, you forget if you sail around in a motor what one has to lug. I wish I could have turned up, if you were waiting, bored, for me to do so, it distressed me, that I couldn't commun, I wanted to leave a message, to write, if I'd realised for a moment you were assuming I'd come, I know I'd wavered so half said I would, I might have rung the hotels, the lodging houses, the tourist office, to locate you, but it's daunting, not second nature to me, to undertake that, you didn't commun with anyone apparently, I had no means of discov your whereabouts, without unnat enterprise, I did want to see you, but had tasks to do, tasks that were more important, consid the lim finan resources, than unnat enterprise. That I couldn't let you know what I was up to wasn't my fault, it was, when it boils down to it, yours. Or you were a bit unreasonable, not to think that I was cut off from you and helpless to remedy it. I'm not reproaching, I'm explaining, but explain sounds like reproach. In May, June, you wrote me long letters, you were there, on the page. But nobody should be impelled, to be there, on the page. And once sitting behind the wheel you have to rush, when at last I could commun, and you were in Venice, where you didn't privately, did you, want me to come, where I'd no intention of coming, dear as Venice is, I thought we could meet for lunch, you were due to pass so close, I could have travelled to meet you for lunch, silly of me, I even had suitable spots in my mind for lunch, out-of-doors and in. You didn't want to stop, it hadn't occurred to you, had it, that it was poss, you didn't consid meeting me at all, by your final evening it was late, to arrange it, I'd tried hard to get hold of you in Venice earlier, but no one thinks of messages that don't materialise. I thought, behind the wheel you have to rush, didn't have much ink. It dawned slowly. As if there had been some displeasure, I sensed. It was unfair. I look at yr letters and feel sad. The commun between us precious. I AM soppy. Diff to grasp, in friendship, what has puffed at it. You don't read my letters any more, what I've already told you by post comes as a surprise. I am froz by this withdrawn cheerfulness.

Because I'm foolhardy, that's why.

It's a toss-up, whether silence is better.

Loathsome, to be calculating, but if we wish to keep the other warm and happ and comfort we can only speak what appeals, and not the unpalatable, we're a lot of saliv dogs, and it's so rewarding, the response to the not unpalatable, we in turn blossom, and so on, on and on. Or we may lean forward at the moment the other leans back, I may lean back, for quite private reasons, a chill inside self, I perceive the embrace and am paralys, am lamed, and no end distressed by that, whilst the one who has leant forward may see something lost, for good, there's a lim to leaning forward, and we all feel froz, and lonelier perhaps. We aren't armed enough against the barely perceptible, before we're aware it's passed. In the dark. One can't get the subjective wrong, exactly, can one. If you think about it. Yet we expect other people not to get things wrong. Until they're got wrong, it's as though one is given extraordin licence, one isn't mis-heard, offence or umbrage isn't taken, one is allowed lapses, of civility, of character, of concentration, one cannot be concentrat all the time, that is understood, and without much warning, or so it appears, the licence is whipped from under one's feet, one goes from being a per in a posit of priv to one very much less grata, one has to brace oneself, but it's too late, something has persuaded one to ignore the warn signs, one simply doesn't believe them, one tries again and again to step past them, and fails, one becomes clumsier, indignant, that one can't step by.

Or you may protest that nothing diff, it's a toss-up, are you taken aback I've thought there is.

I blame nightmares. If we didn't experience such

intense frustration in dreams, and unfairness, if we didn't travel so much in them, and have diff getting in touch, we might not in daylight be so frantic, it's the memory of what has happened in dreams that affects us, it keeps thumping us, is it any wonder. I've a horr idea we seek desolation, we think it is beautiful, we strive towards it, willy-nilly, inner desolat and the desolation of our surroundings. That may be the explanation. There has to be some explan. Then we can only sit on our haunches in the silence and try not to glow.

Glower.

The Hole in the Sky

They certainly look formidable in a garden, are they bitter, I assume they must be, why do they grow so well on furniture, why does furniture want to grow such bitter leaves. I hope you haven't been looking forward to scones & jam. I've made mandelhörnchen, they've come out rather flattened, never mind, eh. I think he has been saying, I shld live in a damp place, where mists don't drag their feet at the door, yes, & tearful fungus climbs the cellar walls, or broods in the roof, white vapours hang quietly above the lawns. He was wondering, what on earth am I doing in a foreign country, why did you have to lug me with you, in the oh so pretty air I at least can't breathe, my lungs are accustomed to moisture. I had to let the snow blow in, for him, blasts of winter, wet, we open windows, all the heatbodies are off, the pipes alone supply us with far more than we are used to, he's been writhing, if I touched him he groaned & shrieked, if you touch him he won't, I'll tell you why, in case you felt cold I warmed us up more & told him we had to be considerate.

I suppose they're the last responsibilities, when there are no animals left, & life is quite unreal, don't you find it unreal yet. A hole in the sky? You don't shave with them. Isn't it a thinning. The warping frightens me. Those are old, but far wider, those new, uninvited. I dreamt in the night I had to hold my most loved horse to be shot. The lid was never like that. It curled up, it was all out of true. I know it's flat now, I'm explaining. Even with an animal one dislikes is one not absolved from these duties, with furniture it isn't so clear cut.

It ought to have done all its writhing, c. 1770, 1800. Too battered & countrified, to be called that, so it's in my eye, it's not beauty but familiarity, I've been looking at it all my life. A crude fellow once hacked away & made acanthus leaves, cruder fellows over the yrs have plugged knot-holes, & screwed in ghastly crude hinges, the old broke, in 1812 some woman pasted a newspaper u. the lid, when she was mixing her paste Beeth. & Hölder. & Gertie were alive, & crude little worms have attacked where no worms shld care to, reduced a tiny oaken world to dust, because that's easier than boring all over it, they riddle tiny worlds & abandon them, exhausted, die out of their own accord, emigrate, or are persecuted to extinction, people have lugged it around, the worm world, him, he's a bit lost, he has the heart of an English bullock, but where has England gone, he can speak because he knows me, sometimes furniture speaks to a stranger. I said to him, you shldn't have planted me in yr bullock's heart, for I am fickle. To me he said, I'd like to see the sun rise day after day & set, before I fall apart, & not be hemmed in by tall buildings, the sun is a vexed question, we've landed ourselves in the prettiest of streets but neither of us is a street person, we like quiet & privacy & our blood flags at the sound of traffic, he is country-born & talks of calling it a day altogether soon, & he has to live with me, compelled to stand meanwhile in a corner. Oh I'm far too uneasy to sit down in it in full view as others do without difficulty!

I said to him, better bury your nose in a book, you're becoming a permanent malcontent. I'm not, actually, I have no home, we don't belong. I think he was telling me he was tired, he hasn't any fellows left, all abandoned, sold or given away, perhaps he has that against me, we cut sad figures, I said. I see no hope for us, no hope at all, there's a horrible moment when one realises it won't do, one has gone astray, mind-bogglingly, the whole of life won't do, making it seem like carelessness. He was wanting to reminisce about draughts & smoking fires

& chilblains, & I had to walk, in the snow, in the woods, on the thick ice, far thicker than his lid, I had to see the trees & their holding of themselves deathly still, & the prints of birds, not dirtied, not squashed, where they led, that they do lead somewhere, he didn't say much when I returned, he would be grumbling to himself, if I touched him he screeched, he couldn't come along, of course he couldn't, he had to stay on his own, he doesn't stretch his legs, it's unfair, I can't help it. One isn't, ever, sure of finding it again, no matter what it may be, the snow, the swans, the woods, the prints of animals & birds, even if it indeed seems to be there, only for a moment can one be sure one is loved, as sure as one can be, it's all down to moments, very insecure, for us too, I told him. He was lonely. I said, loneliness can be put to work. I had to be blunt with him, because what he's homesick for can't be retrieved.

The ice is rucked, over the Havel. Come the summer I'll take you into the forest & show you where my seeds have been growing, in the wild, & say, there's my garden, my sweet peas, smuggled ex England, my himalayan balsam, I'll plant a clematis montana + clod of lime, & old roses, you cld bend to smell them. In humdrum fashion one goes slowly crackers. I wonder if himalayan balsam has the energy to jump into the east.

He hasn't spoken since I gave him the intensive cure, Hun unguents, the lid sits true, the warping is much better. Perhaps I don't recognise my stuff when it gleams uniformly without dust & wax traps. To make his miseries worse, when we came he had to change gender, we sit, separately clouded, watching the sun flood the building opposite, she doesn't murmur, one wouldn't know he'd lived with me all these yrs, I think I have stopped whistling, we take our pleasure in a shaft as it touches the reveal of the N-most window for 14 going on 15 mins. I tell her, in the summer we shall be glad not to be boiled. She doesn't groan any more, thank you, now, your hole in the sky?

Pruning

If a poppy sieds itself in the rhubarb bed you pluck it out.
I suppose you pick your sweet peas? But their intention is
to flower, and flower, they don't stint the flowering, and
pod, you thwart them, you don't let them strew their own
sied, you buy new sied, yet sweet peas are lovely without
going to the hairdresser. You think with your eyes, and
your eyes have been brought up on ideology.

In the Tierpark they have more room.

Is it a question of aesthetics, so much? Or, of understanding. Pods with sieds in them are quite as satisfying
as flowers, you probably view pods, or the sied-down,
with irritation or indulgence, collecting the prettier for
autumn vases. Once a plant has flowered we say it is
over. Over!

They must long to stretch their legs.

You have no doubts, do you, over which are weeds, you
yank things out without a qualm, and receive praise for
it. Instead, nature's ingenuity might be commended. But
no, visitors come into the garden and congratulate the
gardener.

They're so quiet.

A great silence, the birds aren't singing, it's as if there
are no birds. No footprints.

They roar more in the spring?

The freeze grips them too.

It's warm in the elephant house, and we can sit, or will
it make us sad. You hack back a bromble because it's a
bromble, you don't first allow it to bear its fruit. I expect
you take meticulous care of your tools. You never forget
to clean your spade. You may even paint the inside of
your wheelbarrow.

You've noticed how gardening, and methods of, arouses passion in the breast? People become anguished about undisciplined strawberries or unswept greenhouse, they feel in their own persons somewhere what they see in a strange garden. They don't realise it, but they are as upset as they would be by a pony in a sore-rubbing halter. But why neatness, why order, what does it soothe in us, what is deluding us, that grass likes to end with a straight edge? It's not true, that a wobbly end is difficult to look after.

If a shrub grows over a path, you cut it, you want to walk where you've always walked. You could have diverted the path and left the shrub in peace. Must a garden serve us, or might we not sometimes be at its service, if we listened the garden could make good use of our hands, a garden has no hands, we have and we meddle a lot with them. We still have a thing or two to learn, yet we assume the garden can't teach us, can't surprise, is subject to us, bloody know-alls, we tease it and deceive it, extract heroic efforts from it, more than we're entitled to, people lose all morality in a garden, especially in their own.

Clipped?

With clipped not folded wings.

Why seagulls? What is done to the cranes and seagulls to stop their flying off?

But only a fellow who doesn't analyse such things can go about the business of a garden naturally.

Open to the sky they stand behind their names and pictures.

Would we be pink, were we to?

So if the garden is to its gardener a private world, a garden of his imagination, other people's pleasure in it is likely to be a bit spoilt, they are exasperated by not having free passage, arrogant, or humble, along the path, it appears he is selfish, if the others have to live in it, or

on its fringe, too, hovering. Most people expect a garden
to serve them, the garden doesn't mind lumps and tufts
but their toes are wounded, they can't understand, it
looks like wilfulness.

You do that for you, you have no interest in toes.

We can't resist artifice, whatever we touch, and we
touch it all, and feast our eyes upon is wrought, not by
any means from the heart to the heart. It can't be helped
when we are so many, but I'm not sure we should be so
proud of it. The motives are suspect. I wonder if only the
plants and flowers can know what's beautiful. To the
flowers in an ordinary garden, being penned in it must be
akin to having to go to the hairdresser every day and sit
around in curlers, even sleep in them. Perhaps we are
presumptuous, fiddling, with the secateurs, curbing, who
can tell, we can't ask. We are accustomed to imposing
our will and our idea of it on a garden, and impressing our
fellows because it is their idea of it as well. If you were
shocked your roses hadn't been pruned, can you be sure
they enjoy it, you assume they do, gardening as it is
generally understood is a system of learnt responses. Of
forced blooms! All sorts of horticultural instructions
arrive with nursery purchases, yet left alone flowers
come where none is supposed to, they have guts. People
imagine that plants are stationery, plants sied themselves and quarter elsewhere and die out where they
were before. You are restive? Why must cabbages grow in
rows, why may they not put themselves where they
please, even if that means they carry bugs with them that
will latch onto other vegetable and cause those to kiel
over, why shouldn't cabbages lead useful lives, if they are
able, they produce tender greenstuff for the kitchen long
after their heads have been chopped off, and their yellow
bunting is delightful. Your yew hedge, would it rather be
kept back, trimmed twice a year, or allowed to get lush
and glossy, until, magnificent, it has to be hacked at to

shed light on poor humans, wilting in its shadow, and to look like a hen plucked alive, has to shake itself and recover, slowly, yews being lumbering. Its misfortune was to have been planted by a human who intended to suppress it. I don't know. You don't know either, though you think you do. It would have grieved you, to see in my garden how the young apple trees lean, some of them, invited to do without support, we leave aside that they have been graughted onto miserable stock, my unkindness to young fruit trees is in your eyes dotty. A lioness is banging at her partition. Of course soil can't regenerate itself out of nowhere, nothing, without help, unless a river changes its habits or centuries take a big hand in it, but maybe one shouldn't have driven it so hard, to exhaustion, in the first place. You put your paw in a nice sack, full of glie, you plume yourself on the result, you're lazy, you have no love for dung, yet one can, feel a love for dung. All we can say is, if an anarchic garden doesn't quite work a genteel one doesn't either.

Loneliness or boredom or both.

Is one compelled to order nature so as not to seem selfish?

I'm afraid they serve only pots after 2 o'clock.

If, what did you have at home, brooms?, brooms have to be murdered, because they are too many and are choking and shoving, do you, for the smaller brooms that can be rescued intact, or fairly intact, dig 20 holes, where they can do no particular harm, holes not very perfectly dug, in a rush, hot, weary jobs make one rush, and plant the brooms not very perfectly, yet at least giving every broom the chance of life, if only it'll take it, or do you dig those holes properly, three holes however, and plant 3 brooms, and they like being transplanted not a jot, having too-heavy bodies, too wind-catching for their roots, three, casting the rest, all those broomish lives, onto the bonfire? You do the latter, why? Or do you labour to save what you are able to, do you chop up the truly murdered ones so they can be kindling, as if you owed it to them, to let them be of some use, returning as ash, food for the soil?

I'm not mocking myself, or you, the garden makes fun of us, even while we wreck it.

Flowers have no sense of danger. They reach out for light and water, but from weeds, from us, they take no avoiding action, they stand quite still to be strangled and cut, and into the darkness of their own homes couch grass gropes, or a mole, other ambitions. We shouldn't ask, of what good is a sense of a beauty, rather, what use is a sense of danger, flowers do very well without it, and we learn the most petty survival from ours.

Think how a tree behaves, about to be felled, and with no idea of it, as the axe is already falling, and the first screams of the saw. If we could cultivate some of that grace!

You don't want to?

Flowers feel no frustration, no anxiety, they evidently have no dreams, don't dream at all. Serene, swallowed, growing, snipped. But they speak, in little voices, they hear, with little ears. The hunters and the hunted, they dream, they dream their horrible states of mind. A flower inside a cow's stomach still smiles, doesn't understand about digestive juices, it's fair to reckon that flowers are rather limited. The sieds, if ripe, will come out of the cow's bottom and drop to earth, and, perhaps, in its smile the flower has an inkling of that. Yet they have an individuality, it's stupid to imagine you can't tell one flower of a species from another, they are no more or less alike than finches in a brood, or puppies.

Do you frown?

And when we can feel bound to a certain plant, not at its handsomest, so long as it cares to live with us, we may then be growing up a little ourselves, we can say, this is the geum in our border, it happens to be the sole geum, it has its fancy name, it is a geum with reddish petals, it has been having a rest for five years and is in fresh heart facing us again, how pleasing, a geum isn't a dear plant, it might be hoicked up and better bought, but if a couple of other geums arrive from the nursery, because being an engineered geum this has probably been deprived of its ability to make friends, they'll be company for it.

And the mothers bried until their wombs begin to rot, in your society, in ours, a tradition of intact toms and seldom females.

That has nowhere to go, true.

Doctored toms, doctored flowers, both deprived of their scent, by us!

Our sense of spoiling is comic, how hurt we are, we spoil things for each other, and invisibly, seeing one magpie in England spoils the day, I don't suppose they feel that either, flowers, we are burdened with a whole lot of useless emotions, without which we'd be prettier, we are quite idiotic, we spoil in spite of it.

A commotion in the Budapesterstr.

Sirens!

They live in fields of sound. That the music may be polyphonic is no grounds for not listening.

Flowers do.

It hasn't died down.

Do we dream the disappearance of our world, its spoilt cheeks, the bloom smirched, since the 13th century we've thought we could put our finger on it, with our own eyes we see houses where once wild moor, poisons swim not trout in streams, trees die, in our bones we feel that grace, and decency, joy, all is vanished, we live on in unrecognisable surroundings, surrounded by unrecognisable people, for 8 centuries we've felt it, isn't that a bit ridiculous? Is it just a dotty dream? Or is it real, has the little earth no breath left.

Perhaps we have to forget, then, it may be an illusion, everything we understand tells us, urgently, it is not.

Outside it's quiet. An eagle is crying. You're quiet!

Why are we able to dream, for what purpose do we have them, how do dreams serve a dog? I wonder if dogs dream of dogs who are dead, of humans they've loved, we guess they dream of hunting because that's all we can watch. Oh, beyond the chemical answer. I wonder if animals, though they dream, have our trick of being where we are actually not, I doubt it. Humans not stationery. I've got into my head, when one has died it may be lonely. I dream night after night of my dogs, spotted on separate nights they are always painfully pleased to see me, separated, shut up alone. That's silly, if I die with that idea I might take it too literally with me. I wonder what it's like, for an elephant, to die in a zoo, or a hippopotamus, and in a house, with snow at the door. And, if heaven is an idea, sustained by so many fertile imaginations, the bellows below, and if our world finishes, does that bring all those folk in heaven falling out of it?

No one would talk, so, of heaven who believed in it, or in anything, of that kind!

But we will persist in making them. Neither of us knows enough about jungle animals to judge.

Are their shining coats an illusion?

I'm depressed, are you depressed, shall we go, why did we come.

My garden is absolutely cut off from me, and I think, we shall grow apart, we shall miss each other. I'd have given up everything, to have been allowed to stay. Sometimes I believe that's true. It was after all only in the nature of an extraordinary gift. One isn't necessarily so unhappy, I had to go and open my mouth, speech isn't very free anywhere.

Let us, shall we, say, we are having one last walk around our separate gardens, instead of these paths and enclosures our borders, shrubs, trees and grass, although we can't be private, and have no gardens.

In the winter, when the trees first and blades of grass are stiff with frost, and one's breathing, white, and one fieds the birds, the blackbirds, dunnock, the pair of blue titmice, chaffinches, and one supposes, I have fed the birds, one walks on, farther, to the dyke, still in one's own garden, behind one that peculiar sound, of the feast, of feather on the air, and one discovers huddled on branches, on one's own frozen branches, blue titmice, chaffinches, the pair of blackbirds, dunnock, starving, forced to listen. They are motionless. They look at one. Every assumption is terrible.

Also published by Serpent's Tail

Dreaming of Dead People
Rosalind Belben

This is an intimate portrait of a woman approaching middle-age, lonely, starved of love, yet avoiding the seductions of resentment. First published ten years ago and now reissued in paperback by Serpent's Tail, *Dreaming of Dead People* is a joyful, stark novel by one of the most distinctive voices of contemporary fiction.

'Rosalind Belben's eye for the movement and texture of the natural world is extraordinarily acute and she has a poet's ear for language. Her book, although apparently a cry of loneliness and deprivation, is also a confession of fulfilment, of endless curiosity for, and love of, life.' SELINA HASTINGS, *Daily Telegraph*

'[Belben's] heroine is a solitary woman who is suffering as she reconciles herself to loneliness and sterility. She tells of her past and recalls, often, the countryside, where being alone is not painful and, if there is no meaning to life, the call to the senses is immediate.' HILARY BAILEY, *The Guardian*

'So extraordinarily good that one wants more, recognizing a writer who can conjure an inner life and spirit, can envisage, in unconnected episodes, a complete world: one unified not by external circumstances but by patterns of the writer's mind.'
ISABEL QUIGLY, *Financial Times*

160 pages £6.95 (paper)

Also published by Serpent's Tail

The Seven Deadly Sins
Alison Fell (ed.)

'Seven fine writers, seven vices probed to the quick.
Splendid.' ANGELA CARTER

'These seven writers represent . . . a newer and more
knowing feminist strategy . . . Mischievous and
exhilarating.' LORNA SAGE, *The Observer*

'Rich in experiment and imagination, a sign of just
how far contemporary women's writing might go.'
HELEN BIRCH, *City Limits*

'All of these stories cut deeply and with a sharp edge
into the main business of life — death, God and the
devil.' RICHARD NORTH, *New Musical Express*

'A rich but random survey of recent women's
writing.' JONATHAN COE, *The Guardian*

'An exciting, imaginative mix of stories.'
ELIZABETH BURNS, *The List*

'Witty, modern, female.'
KATHLEEN JAMIE, *Scotland on Sunday*

'Extremely entertaining.'
EMMA DALLY, *Cosmopolitan*
240 pages £7.00 (paper)